5.95

I'm Done Crying

I'M DONE CRYING

BY

LOUANNE FERRIS

as told to Beth Day

PUBLISHED BY

M. EVANS AND COMPANY, INC.

NEW YORK

AND DISTRIBUTED IN ASSOCIATION WITH

J. B. LIPPINCOTT COMPANY

PHILADELPHIA AND NEW YORK

Foreword

How I met "Louanne Ferris" is not important; nor is the fact that both these names are the names I gave her in order to hide her identity.

What is important is her reality. Courage, beauty, and the kind of joy that refuses to be quieted by the heavy hand of tragedy that somehow went into the making of her. Not for years has any one person made such an impression on me.

It took five months to tape record her story and then another five months to shape it into this book. I use the word "shape" advisedly, for the words are Louanne's. So are the warmth and eloquence.

In the beginning I was interested only in Louanne's life as a nurse. I saw her as part of a city hospital where things too terrible to believe too frequently happen. Now, I know the whole woman. And I know that her experience belongs to the larger world of injustice and indifference in which all of us live.

Exposure to her triumphant soul has left me full of new hope.

Beth Day

CHAPTER ONE

The Road
to the Hospital

I became a nurse by pure chance. And there's been many a moment, especially when I'm the one who has to hold the dying patient in my arms because his family won't do it, and he's still alert and looking into my eyes, that I wonder why I didn't become a policewoman instead. Or a file clerk, or anything else that wouldn't eat your heart out every living day.

There were eleven of us kids. I don't remember much about my mother except the pongee dress she was wearing the day she was buried. And her string of red crystal beads. One of my older sisters cut the beads into eight parts—by then there were only eight of us left—and gave each of us a section of beads to

7

remember her by. That's all I ever had that belonged to my mother.

One of my older brothers does remember her. He remembers that she was gentle, quiet, wore the same dress to church each Sunday, was always pregnant, and died in childbirth. I was four years old at the time.

Our father worked as a gardener for white families in a southern city. What I remember most about him was how the biscuits would get cold at dinner while he was saying grace. He'd start out with an ordinary prayer, then if we heard him let out a laugh, we knew he would soon be shouting and singing—and there'd be no food for another fifteen minutes. If one of us giggled he'd beat the hell out of us, then go right on praying, and we wouldn't get our dinner till he was finished. After my mother died, my father farmed out the youngest of us kids to relatives and married again. My stepmother was a good-looking woman but a real bitch. I never did stay with them over a few months at a time and I was always glad to leave.

He sent my younger sister and me to a childless uncle and aunt who lived on a farm. He never did pay them anything for keeping us. He'd come around every few months to visit, crying and praying and shouting, but he never left a nickel for our keep.

They got their money's worth out of me, though. There wasn't a job on that farm too mean for me, hoeing or haying or feeding the stock. I'll never forget those winter mornings when I'd stumble out to the barns to milk the cows. I was just a little kid, and so cold and sleepy and not enough clothes to keep warm. I finally did figure out a way to cheat so I could get finished faster. I'd milk halfway up the bucket, then fill it with water. They never did catch me, or else they surely would have killed me.

They weren't nearly so hard on Sis. She had lighter skin than I do, and better hair. We hadn't been on the farm long before they took in another niece and nephew. But I was still the underdog. If my aunt made a cake or pie she'd give the pan to Sis and her other niece to lick and if I got any it was because Sis gave me part of hers. Once when the two girls were finishing up a sweet potato pie, Sis took her dirty finger and smeared off a swipe of it and stuck it in my face. I slapped her dirty hand away from my mouth and the custard splashed on the floor. My aunt made me lick it up off the wooden planks.

The only day in the week I liked was Sunday. Religion meant a lot to me from the time I was just a little kid—I guess to help make up for the things I didn't have. I liked to go to church. Any church. I'm not prejudiced about religion. We have a Catholic chapel at the hospital and one that is used for the Protestants and Jews, and I drop into whichever one I'm closest to when I find a moment to pray.

That strong religious feeling helped me get through a lot of things. I remember when I was about eight years old I had a cluster of warts on the back of my right hand which bothered me. Neither my aunt nor uncle paid any attention to it, so I talked about it to a teacher who was temporarily boarding at the farm. She told me to take the Bible and hold it in my right hand and say a prayer every morning for sixteen mornings. With my already being something of a religious fanatic that was really my stick. Every morning I took out the Bible and said my prayer. After two weeks, the warts disappeared. The teacher had left by then and I never told anyone what had happened. That was my secret. I felt that God had laid His hand on me. It seemed to me that the best way I could ever express my religion would be to try to help other people, since He had helped me.

My uncle had a good singing voice, and before the years of tonsilitis and yelling took their toll I had a pretty good alto voice myself, and we used to sing solos in church. I also recorded the minutes for the Sunday School and read them out before the congregation each Sunday. I never was plagued with being bashful.

The best part of church was the music and the worst part was the preachers. You've heard all those jokes about the parson getting the choice pieces of the Sunday chicken. Well, they're true. It's enough to turn your stomach to see the way the poor people in the South cater to a preacher, and make over him like he's a little god. When the preacher came to the farm to dinner—and it didn't have to be Sunday either—my aunt would give him the very best of the meat or chicken or turkey or whatever we had—and woe be to us hungry kids if we tried to get anything to eat before he was finished. I used to puzzle about preachers —if they really were men of God, then wouldn't they be wanting to share with people instead of taking it away from them? I often wondered what would have happened if God Himself had turned up for dinner. I guess my aunt would have just shot the lot of us to make sure we wouldn't try to get any of the food for ourselves.

When the bishop came around it was even worse. Those farm women who couldn't buy enough sugar to give their families pie once a month would bake for days ahead, so that the little one-room church was lined on both sides with long tables heaped with cakes and pies. That old fat-bellied bishop would come in, patting heads (and a butt or two if he could get away with it) and make his way down the tables, sampling anything that caught his eye, while we kids were lucky to steal a muffin.

When I got up North, I found, to my surprise, it wasn't much better there. The first city church I attended with a friend of mine, was a poor little storefront one-room church in the black ghetto. The congregation was so poor they couldn't feed or clothe their own children properly, yet their minister drove a Cadillac and sent his own kids to the best schools. The church held "pound night" once a month and those poor stupid mothers, who didn't have milk for their own children, would each donate a pound of food "to the church." Where they ever thought their donations went was what puzzled me.

And when the little congregation would stand up

and start to sway and sing it was like being back in that church in Alabama. They could really make music. Warm, human, real. Soul music. The same kind of music that singers like Elvis Presley and Aretha Franklin have made popular with white audiences.

Music is one way I know I'm human. When I feel the tears come down my cheeks when I sing, or when I hear something funny and find that I can laugh, then I know I'm alive.

Sundays have always been like a pearl to me, the beautiful part of the week. Most of my adult life I've had to work on Sundays. But the times I haven't— those rare days that I spent going to church and singing, and then just lazing around home, cooking soul food for my family—those are the good days of my life.

It was looking forward to Sundays that made my life on the farm bearable. But I hated it there the rest of the time. When I was ten years old and one of my older sisters who was married and living in Birmingham came to visit, I cried so hard she took me home with her. There wasn't any truant officer in the neighborhood she lived in, so instead of sending me to school, she put me out as a live-in maid with a white family. I guess they felt bad about my not getting any schooling, so their kids tutored me each day when they got home from their classes. The whole family was good to me and I would have liked to have stayed with them but my sister's husband lost his job and they moved to Detroit, and before they left she put me to live with a Negro teacher. This woman was divorced and had two little kids and it was my job to take total charge of the house and kids. But I was allowed to go to school. By this time I was twelve years old and I had got enough out of my tutoring that they let me enter the eighth grade.

When I finally did get to go to school I surely did love it. I was the kind of kid who always had my hand in the air when I wasn't powdering my nose. But the black teachers in the South in those days were chicken. They kept their jobs by pleasing the white city fathers, and seeing to it that the Negro schools ran smoothly. They didn't encourage anyone who asked too many questions. I got kicked out of science class for challenging the teacher's statements about God. Then, when I was fourteen I joined the NAACP and one day I showed up at school wearing a button they had distributed to their members. It read ABOLISH THE POLL TAX. The principal of the school spotted me, and he called me up in front of the assembly and pointed to my button.

"Do you realize what you are doing?" he asked me.

Then, before I could answer, he threw a comical look at the other kids and said, "You could get yourself hung for that!"

Of course everybody laughed because he was making fun of me. I thought what a gutless, stupid fool he was, but there wasn't much I could do about it. We could have had student revolts in those days too, except there was nobody on my side.

I didn't have any close friends. And certainly no

guidance. One woman, the sister of the teacher I lived with, I was beginning to like very much until the day she shot her husband.

We shared a yard—her house was in back of ours and I was doing mathematics at the kitchen table one afternoon with supper started on the stove, when I heard a shot. I looked up in time to see a figure, with a gun in hand, sneak through the hedge. She was wearing man's clothes but I recognized her. Her husband was lying in the grass, alive but wounded. The police came and the ambulance and they carried him off to the hospital. She was the first one there to see him, crying and weeping over him. He never did know who shot him. But I knew and she knew that I knew. "If you hadn't been sitting there at the table, where I was afraid I'd hurt you, I might have got him!" she told me one day, with a laugh. But I didn't think it was funny. I was scared of her after that.

I was fifteen years old and a junior in high school when I married a boy named Judson. Nobody believes me when I say I was the kind of girl who thought marriage was kissing and going off into the sunset holding hands. But it's God's truth. I had already known some hardships in my life, but I didn't have a clue about the hardships that go with marriage.

I still know why I married Judson. I wanted something of my own and I thought I was in love with him. Nobody knows why he married me, though, least of all his mother. You may think you've seen all there is about prejudice when you see it between Caucasian and Negro. But, baby, you haven't seen how rough prejudice can be until you've experienced it Negro to Negro. I don't say black to black, because that's what it's all about: all those shades of black.

Judson's family were not truly mulatto (half white and half black) but there was a lot of white blood in the family and he was the lightest skinned of them all. Looking back from where I sit now, I really do believe that's why he never amounted to anything in this world. His Mama was so proud of him and had him so spoiled, he thought all he ever had to do was just *be.*

We fought the first day. He wanted us to go move in with his Mama and his sisters and I refused. We ended up moving in with the teacher where I was living. Judson finished high school and got a job as a porter. And I got pregnant.

I was young and strong, and I didn't have much trouble except for a long labor. When they finally delivered me, the white nurse held my baby up where I could see him and said, "Just looky here. You got yourself a white baby!"

I suppose she thought she was paying me some kind of compliment. She couldn't know how much her words cut me. The baby, we named him Billy, looked just like his father. Fair-skinned, straight-haired, handsome. Me, I'm as dark brown as a newly roasted coffee bean.

Judson never did stick to any job over a few weeks, which should have been a pretty good clue how our life was going to play out. But then World War II came along and he went overseas. By that time I was pregnant again. Judson never did see that baby, a second boy we named Martin, until five years later, after the war was over.

Many of the southern Negroes who didn't go into service went north looking for defense jobs, among them my two older brothers, Bill and Jim. After they got themselves established, they wrote me, urging me to bring my babies and join them. They told me I wouldn't have any trouble getting a job, and then when Judson did get home, it would be easier for him to find work there, too. It made sense to me. Besides, I thought putting some miles between Judson and his Mama might not be such a bad idea either.

By that time, our first baby, Billy, was a lively four-year-old. Bright eyed, quick and cute, he was into everything. He missed his Daddy and every time he saw a soldier go by he'd run and grab him by the pants leg and squawl, "That's my Daddy!" He chased down so many soldiers I finally had to get him one of those little harnesses with a leash. The day we left the South, I had Billy in his harness, and the baby in my arms when we went to the railroad station. It was jam-packed with soldiers and civilians like all stations were in those years and I found us a corner where the children wouldn't be trampled. Just then, a soldier walked past. Well, Bill ran for him, tackled one leg and whooped, "Here's my Daddy!" He had a powerful voice for a child his age and a number of people looked around to see what he was screaming about.

16

I was hauling him off the soldier's leg, when I happened to glance up into the man's face. I nearly died. He was white. He tried to smile but it came off pretty thin.

By the time I joined my brothers, Jim had found an apartment for me in a three-family building on the edge of the black ghetto. Although the ghetto proper began only ten buildings away from us, our particular building was neat and nice, and our apartment was roomy. It had an entrance foyer, with the bathroom off that, a hall bedroom, living room, kitchen and large bedroom. Jim, who was a bachelor with a full-time job in a garage, intended to keep the hall bedroom for himself and share the apartment, and the rent, with me. My brother Bill by this time had found himself a wife: a lovely, gentle girl named Alice whom I liked the moment we met, and they were living in a building about six blocks away, in easy walking distance of us. Then only weeks after I arrived, Sis trailed me north, and moved in with Jim and me and the boys. This was a break for me, to have my family all so close. I was more fortunate than most young ghetto mothers because Sis and Jim could help watch the kids for me, when I found a job.

After the South, the city at first seemed very dirty and ugly to me. Somehow I had pictured it as just a larger version of the pretty suburbs of Birmingham, neat and green and well-tended. Actually, the area I moved into looked much better at that time than it does now. Many of the ghetto houses had nice little yards and back gardens in those days. Since then, the area has deteriorated so that there doesn't seem to be anything in the yards but trash. Our apartment faced a wide avenue, which had a number of small stores and a school. Today, most of the little stores have disappeared. The man who owned the drugstore on the corner when I moved in was robbed so many times that he finally closed down. The butcher where I bought meat when I first moved to the city was shot to death two years ago.

Even the sky in the city seemed different to me than it had back home. In Alabama the nights were velvet and the stars so sparkling and close you feel you can reach out and touch them. In the city everything that was pretty seemed distant and out of reach. The dirty air, the dirt-filled streets, the harsh noises all grated on me.

The first week I found a job in a small feather hat factory close to us where I could walk to and from work. My hours worked out so that either Jim or Sis could look after the boys for me when I wasn't home. But a few days pasting feathers together was enough for me. I wanted to be where the action was. I wanted to work around people.

I was complaining about my job to one of our neighbors who lived on the first floor of our building, a little spitfire of a woman named Lettie who worked as an aide at the city hospital that served this area, and she suggested, "Why not come to the hospital with me in the morning and apply for a job there?"

At this point, the only hospital I had ever been in

was the one I went to to have my two babies. It was segregated, of course, but the ward was nice and clean and, like all good OB wards, it had a pleasant feeling about it, an air of happiness that came from all the proud mothers and the little newborns. I thought I'd like to work in a place like that.

"But I haven't any training," I told Lettie. "I didn't even finish high school."

"Don't you worry!" she laughed. "They'll take anything with two legs and two arms that can hobble down a corridor and carry a tray."

She told me to be ready the next morning at seven. Since neither my brother Jim nor Sis were going to be home that morning, I had to take my little boys with me. I had walked to work on my other job, so I had not as yet experienced what wartime rush-hour public transportation in the city was like.

Lettie explained to me that it took forty-five minutes to get from our building to the hospital, however you sliced it. You could take two buses, or you could walk the shortest leg of the route, which was about eight blocks, and catch the second bus. We decided to walk the first part and save the extra fare. We were standing on the corner, waiting, each carrying a child, when the bus appeared. I couldn't believe it. There were so many people already packed inside that bodies bulged out of the open windows. I backed away from the curb. I wasn't even going to try to get on that bus, until Lettie gave me a sharp shove in the back. "Get on, get on," she insisted. "Push your way in."

I did as she insisted and, each of us with a child

held high where he couldn't suffocate, we pushed ourselves up the steps onto the bus. It was a thirty-minute ride, through the very heart of the ghetto. Outside the bus windows, I caught an occasional glimpse of the rows of dilapidated frame and brick tenements that lined both sides of the street. Dirt and refuse clogged the vacant lots and gutters. Mangy, skinny dogs and cats scavenged the windblown trash that piled against the chicken-wire fences. A rat, the size of a hound pup, skittered boldly down the gutter as we paused at a stoplight.

By the time we had arrived at the hospital bus stop, Lettie and I had, bit by bit, been shoved to the very back of the bus by the pressure of more bodies pushing in from the front.

Lettie yanked the cord. "Getting off! Getting off!" she screamed, charging her way toward the front. I followed in her wake, a little more discreetly, trying not to permanently injure anyone I passed.

Then Lettie hit an immovable object, a plump, middle-aged woman who either could not, or would not, give way.

Lettie gave her a sharp shove.

"You quit shoving, you dirty nigger!" the woman screamed.

"Get out of my way, you Christ-killing Jew!" Lettie screamed back at her.

I was frozen with shock. I had never in my life heard such an exchange between black and white. In the South of my childhood there simply wasn't any.

The lines were clearly drawn. Negroes grew up knowing "their place" and most of them kept in it.

As Lettie continued to push until she squeezed past, the woman hauled off and took a swing at her, missed, and caught me across the back of the neck. It didn't hurt much and I just wanted to get off that bus. Personally I thought both of them were in the wrong: Lettie for pushing so rudely, and the other woman for being so hostile. And after the names they had exchanged, I figured they were even. But when Lettie saw the woman strike me, she figured she still owed her one. So she turned around and spat in her face. As the bus pulled away from the curb, the last thing I saw was that woman's livid, angry face, with the mucous dripping down it.

By that time I was ready to turn tail and run home and forget the whole business. My little boys were so terrified by the crush and the scene that they weren't even crying. They just stood there, round-eyed and speechless.

But Lettie's good spirits had apparently returned. "Come along, Louanne," she said, tugging impatiently at my arm. "The nursing office is right over here. I'll take you there before I check in."

I followed her in silence, wondering if I ever would adjust to such dog-eat-dog city life. Alabama seemed quiet and pretty and far away.

I was still shaking when I walked into the nursing office and applied for a job. Lettie was right. They didn't ask me about my education, experience, or qualifications. All they wanted to know was when I could start work.

I promised to be at the hospital the following morning at seven-thirty.

CHAPTER *TWO*

Nobody Knows
Their Names

I walked into the main kitchen on the first floor of the hospital the other morning, and it really took me back in time. There was that same big hole in the floor between one of the stoves and the long work table that was there the first morning I came to work, over twenty-two years ago! It's an irregular patch of missing tile about three feet in diameter, the shape of Texas, with one long, narrow section, like the Panhandle, which stretches out nearly five feet directly in front of the stove where the cooks stand.

That hole is always filled with several inches of filthy water. In fact, the entire kitchen floor runs like a river, with patches of grease slick spotted here and there as though a freighter had just passed by. They are never able to get rid of the water because they wash down the big food drums with hoses, and the drains in the floor stay so clogged they can't absorb the runoff. I have never seen the kitchen floor dry, nor have I ever known the temperature of the room to vary from around ninety-nine degrees, winter or summer.

The kitchen staff is made up entirely of men. I guess the administrators figure the women would be more likely to faint from the heat. When the men complain about getting arthritis from standing on a wet floor all day, they are told to wear rubber boots on the job. But the only worker I ever knew of who did try wearing boots slipped and fell in the greasy water and suffered a permanent back injury.

It isn't that conditions like that don't get reported. I'm sure that every mayor of this city in the past twenty years has had a health department report on his desk, citing, among other problems in our hospital, that particular hole in the kitchen floor. And, in all fairness, I suppose some of the mayors have ordered that something be done about it. Every once in a while we get an investigating committee coming through the hospital. But it's usually the same old story. The members of the committee become "incensed." They make statements to the press. Then maybe someone shows up to fix one of the broken dishwashing machines or somebody else comes along with a can of fresh paint for the reception room. Then it all gets swept under the rug again till the next investigation.

24

Time and again I've wondered why the city doesn't let each hospital's engineering department have just a little old petty cash fund. Then when a nurse reports to our engineer that the sterilizer in the nursery isn't working and he finds it needs a fifty cent part he could go out and buy one. The way it is now, he has to turn in a requisition. I don't know where the city files requisitions but it must be in someone's mattress, because they always get lost for at least five months. Then the nurse yells and screams and says another baby has died and what are they going to do about it and the engineer tells her he already asked for that part to fix the sterilizer, but he'll ask again. Well, maybe a month or so after he puts in the second requisition he does get the part and he fixes the sterilizer. And nobody but the nurse and the parents remember about that baby. Because nobody knows the names of city hospital patients anyway.

Patients in city hospitals are not people. They are numbers. When a doctor comes on a floor he doesn't say, *who* do you have new today? He says, "How many admissions are there?" He's figuring the *number* of patients he will have to handle that day. The other hospital workers, the nurses and the aides, usually refer to the patients as "the census." They estimate the burden of their job in terms of the day's census: how many beds to be made that day; how many trays to be prepared, how many X-rays to be taken. When the patients line up for treatment, their names are not recorded and then called out as they would be in a private clinic. The aide gives them a number just as butchers do in crowded meat markets.

City hospitals are seldom a thing of beauty except for those projected on the city architectural department's drawing boards, and our hospital is no exception. A cluster of five big, old, five-story brick buildings, each built around a central concrete court, the hospital stretches out over a full city block. Located in an old, dirty, commercial section of the city bordering the ghetto it is separated from the neighboring small businesses, and the school next door, by a high iron fence. Outside the neurosurgical building, at the entrance leading to the nursing supervisor's office, there is still a trace of human hair on the iron pickets, where a patient impaled himself leaping from the fourth floor ward above. For months after the suicide, there were also traces of human tissue on the spikes until we got our first good rain. I always wondered how our nursing supervisor—a woman so fastidious she washes the silver before she'll eat her lunch—could walk past that fence each morning without demanding that someone fetch a bucket and clean it off. But I guess you can get used to anything.

If you look closely at the outside of any one of the hospital buildings, you will see torn, rusted screens at the windows. They stay on winter and summer, year in and year out, just like the hole in the kitchen floor. I have never seen anyone either remove or repair one.

Usually when you walk into the admissions building, which faces the main street, you will find fifty or sixty people wandering around the wide marble receiving room. The ones that got there first occupy the three small wooden benches which make up the room's total furnishings. The rest mill about, or lean against the walls or pay the vending machine fifteen cents for a small, bad cup of coffee. There is no lunch room or cafeteria for visitors or family. The nearest food is a commercial coffee shop across the street where a hamburger costs fifty-five cents.

There is always someone mopping the dirty floor with a musty mop that has been dipped into a harsh, evil-smelling disinfectant. Children of various sizes race around the room, periodically restrained by parents or guards.

Beyond the french doors, on the inner side of the room, there is a grassy court which would make a nice playground for the children, but the doors are kept locked. The court is empty except for the pieces of stale cake, candy wrappers and wine bottles that the patients throw down from the upper windows.

And of course there is the pigeon population. Every health department report on city hospitals complains about the "pigeon excreta" which frosts the roofs and window ledges of the hospital buildings. Since we only have air conditioning in one of the operating rooms, and have to keep most all the windows open in hot weather, the pigeon droppings are considered a health hazard. Over the years there have been some feeble attempts to scare off the pigeons, but they always come back. There are still a few Italian families living in the neighborhood and wherever you find Italians, you find a vigorous pigeon population, since they raise them on the roofs of their apartments. When I first came to this area we had many more Italian families than we do now. There were also some Irish and Jewish families. Now it is predominantly Negro and Puerto Rican.

The first morning I checked into the hospital, to work, I was told to report to the Male Ward as a kitchen aide. It was a sunny, pretty May morning and I had recovered from my shock of the day before, and was looking forward to my new job. I liked the idea of serving people and my head was full of visions of smiling nurses in starched white uniforms holding pretty babies as I took the elevator to the third floor male ward. At the third floor I asked the operator for the nurses' station and was told it was at the far side of the main ward, past the large swinging doors that opened off the end of the corridor. As I walked toward the doors, I noticed that there were two smaller wards to my right and left. The doors to both were open and as I passed by I glanced in the one on my left; momentarily froze, and kept on walking. Then I looked to see if anyone was watching me and, since no one was in sight, I turned around and went back to get another sneaky look to make sure if it was really true.

There were eight beds in the room. In each bed sat a little old man. Their flesh long since melted away by age, they looked like stick figures—their legs no more than thin slats of kindling wood against the white of the bed linen. They had all apparently pushed off their covers during the night and the top sheets and blankets were on the floor. So were the bedpans, some of them overflowing, their contents spilled out in haphazard puddles.

All the men were awake. They were all sitting up in bed, their bony little knees akimbo, their hospital gowns around their waists, so that every age-atrophied penis and scrotum was clearly visible from the corridor. That, I guess, was what had brought me back for a second look. I couldn't believe that a hospital would allow its patients to look like that.

I walked on slowly down the hall. At the big doors that opened into the main ward, I took a steadying deep breath, then walked in.

The entire room had been painted, at some distant time, in a sickening, bilious yellow-green color that was now flaked and peeling. The windows and window sills were thick with dirt. Some windows had torn shades; others had none. The ceiling was leprous with dark brown spots—which I later learned were made by the doctors and nurses when they tested syringes by squirting medication into the air. I was to see those same brown spots year in and year out. In fact, they are still there.

There were thirty men in this ward. A quick glance showed that they were, unlike the men in the eight-bed ward who had all appeared ancient, of varying

29

ages. They, too, were all sitting up in bed, although it was barely seven in the morning. Some of them had on no clothing. Others had their hospital gowns hitched at various levels of exposure. They stared at me without expression, their eyes dull and ill above the stubble of their beards. Again, some of the older or sicker patients' legs caught my attention. They looked no more than two inches in circumference, the skin hanging slack from the bone. Bedpans and urinals cluttered the floor; the combined smell of feces, stale urine, and the food that patients kept in their night stands was overpowering.

I looked at the back of the room, where I saw a nurse sitting at a desk, head bowed over a report, writing. How could she just sit there, I wondered, with so much to do? Could she be indifferent to this hell in front of her? I had never been around really sick people before. I just hadn't realized anyone could live like this. Controlling the urge to turn and run out, I made myself walk down to where the nurse sat.

When I gave her my name, she told me that I was to work in Male Medicine, but on the other side of the building, and told me how to get there. I walked back through the ward, wondering if the other side could be this bad.

It was. When I found my way around to the other wing I encountered the same conditions. It amazed me to see other workers hurrying by, janitors, aides, nurses, all of them apparently indifferent to the sights and smells that stunned me.

When I reported to the nurses' station in this wing, the floor nurse looked up, gave me a quick, sharp glance of appraisal, then said, "Follow me. I'll show you where you'll work."

As she rose from the desk, I could almost hear the band strike up a march. Trim, flat-hipped, starchily crisp, she was the perfect army nurse, a dynamo in uniform, with a sharp, authoritative voice that plainly said, "Don't give me any crap. I'm busy."

Obviously Irish, her hair was black and curly, her eyes a very pretty blue. But that was the end of it as far as beauty was concerned. Her head was hunched on her square shoulders like a frog's, with no neck in between. Her uniform fell slack over her flat, masculine body. Her name, she told me, was Kilpatrick.

She led me to a narrow, rectangular room across from one of the small, eight-bed wards. It had a refrigerator, a work table and a hot plate. There was no real cooking done in the ward diet kitchens, Kilpatrick explained. The food came up on trucks from the main kitchen below and was dished up and served there. They kept fruit juice in these ward kitchens, as well as bread for toast, tea and eggs. They were also supposed to make coffee here but the machine was broken so the coffee had to be brought up from below too. (The machine still is broken.)

When Kilpatrick left, I opened the refrigerator door to see what stock I had. Among the pitchers of fruit juice and containers of eggs, I saw bottles of blood and medications. Water dripping from the ice com-

31

partment down through the lower shelves had made
several of the written labels on the bottles illegible,
completely destroyed others. Bits of melted paper
from the labels, as well as dried splashes of fruit juice,
milk and blood spotted the floor of the refrigerator.
I was cleaning it out with a rag when a sharp-featured
little nurse, with crisp blue-gray curls framing her
white cap, whizzed into the room, reached past my
head for one of the egg baskets and a container of
milk. I watched, puzzled, while she broke five of the
eggs into a pitcher, added milk, then pulled a small
flask out of her pocket and stirred in a good half cup
from it. I recognized the smell of bourbon.

She poured the mixture into an oversized glass and
trotted out into the hall. She had not said a word to
me.

Kilpatrick stuck her head in the door. "The breakfast truck will be up in five mintes. You've got a census
of sixty-two to feed today. Some of them are supposed
to be on special diets but we haven't got a dietician
this month so forget it. Give them whatever they think
they can eat."

As her black head flashed out of sight, I ran after
her. "Excuse me, Miss Kilpatrick," I said, "but a nurse
came in and took five eggs—"

"—and made an eggnog for her baby," Kilpatrick
finished with a grimace. "That's the floor supervisor,
Miss Adams. She's got a crush on Dr. Brown in pediatrics. She nursed him through pneumonia last Janu-
ary, and she's been taking him an eggnog every day
since 'to keep his strength up.' "

"But what about the patients' eggs?"

Kilpatrick shrugged. "Probably a lot of them won't want eggs. Feed them cereal—or whatever they send up." She hurried on down the corridor.

I went back into my kitchen, to get out my supplies. There were only twenty plates and the drawer for silver contained twenty forks and thirty spoons. There were no knives. How was I supposed to feed sixty-two men with twenty plates and forks? And what would I do for knives at lunch if the meat was tough? . . .

I soon learned what you do about the plates and forks. You serve twenty patients, then run around to the first and start grabbing up the plates and silver as fast as they have finished with them; wash them by hand, and serve the next twenty.

I started the serving of breakfast with some concern—wondering if the wards would still be in such foul shape when the patients ate. But at nine o'clock screens were put in front of the doors and the nurse's aides cleaned up the night's mess, made up the beds, washed the patients, and got them tucked in again. Within an hour or two some of the oldest and most senile had their covers back on the floor, their matchstick legs once again dangling perilously over the bedrails.

The patients in Male Medicine ranged in age from twelve to ninety. Boys below twelve were placed in the Pediatric Ward. A number of the old men were not, I discovered, really ill at all. They were merely senile. Either their families could not keep them or they had no families. There was nowhere else to go.

Some had been there days, others weeks, and even months. Drifters, winos, old men who had simply outlived their wives and families, nameless and homeless, they were waiting to die.

They did not belong with the ill patients. Nor did they require the same medical care. They were in the hospital only because the hospital could not refuse them. I wondered then, as I have wondered since, why it would not prove better economy in the long run for the city to build a nursing home on the hospital grounds, where these old folk could be cared for by medically less skilled employees who had more time to be kind, and relieve the crowding within the buildings designed and staffed to care for the sick?

It seemed as though I had just finished getting my patients all fed their breakfast and the mess cleaned up, when the lunch truck arrived. In those days employees of the hospital still got two meals per day free. The moment the lunch truck appeared at the kitchen, nurses and aides swarmed on it, armed with empty gallon coffee cans, and began picking out all the best meat for themselves and their friends. The kitchen had sent up plenty, but it began to disappear at an alarming rate. After all the other nurses and aides had taken theirs and gone, one big, tough-looking sister just kept standing there, piling piece after piece of meat into her bucket, until I couldn't stand it any longer.

"You ought to be ashamed!" I said. "You can go out and buy a hamburger if you're hungry. But this is all the patients have to eat, and you're stealing all of it!"

34

She turned on me, her fork in the air, her eyes narrowed in anger. "You meet me outside, baby. I'm going to beat you up." She finished picking out the last of the good pieces, turned and stalked away.

I was scared. She was a big, powerful-looking woman, a lot heavier and stronger than I was. Her voice was deep as a man's. While I was serving my first twenty patients, I worried over what I should do. I figured she meant she'd be waiting for me when I left the hospital that night and I didn't have anything with me to protect myself. I decided to find a pair of surgical scissors to carry in my pocket before I left for home.

But that wasn't easy. There were no scissors in supply. Each nurse bought her own pair and carried it with her. During the afternoon I noticed a short, young male aide who was working on my floor using scissors to cut tape. He was a kind-faced fellow, with sort of mulatto coloring and straight black hair (I later learned he was Japanese but these were war years and neither he nor his friends made any mention of the fact). I had heard Kilpatrick call him Teddy. So, as soon as I caught him in the corridor, with no one else around, I stopped him and introduced myself.

"I just started here today, Teddy," I said, hoping to catch his sympathy.

It worked. He gave me a nice, open smile. "If you need any help, let me know."

"Could I borrow your scissors?" I asked. "I didn't realize you had to bring your own."

"They're not much," Teddy smiled, "but you're

35

welcome to them." He handed me his pair of battered, broken scissors. It apparently didn't occur to him to ask what a kitchen aide needed with them.

I thanked him and slipped them into the pocket of my uniform.

I had looked forward to getting acquainted with at least two or three patients individually my first day. But as the hours flew by, while I tried to keep up with the silver shortage, and get the meals dished up and served to my patients, and the special orders of tea and toast prepared for those who couldn't face the hospital menu, I realized that it was impossible. The patients, so far, were nothing more to me than rows of stubbled faces and dull, blank eyes. As the day drew to a close the sad thought occurred to me that I had not learned a single patient's name. No wonder the doctors I saw rushing down the corridors, their blood-streaked white coats flapping, and the nurses running distractedly from one ward to another with emergency equipment in their hands, spoke of the patients as "admissions"; "the census"; "today's patient load." So many bodies to tend, so many beds to make, or, in my case, so many mouths to feed.

When visiting hours arrived I was pleased to see that quite a few of our patients had callers, family members or friends. I noticed as they passed my kitchen that almost every visitor carried some kind of package.

Then the smells began to reach me. Following my nose, I entered the main ward. It was like walking into an international delicatessen: the singular odors of garlic, chicken fat, chitlings filled the air. The visitors had brought in everything from entire pizzas to collard greens. There was fried chicken, spaghetti, Jewish cheese cake, pigs' feet. I even saw one old black man tenderly unwrap a baked sweet potato. What they didn't eat then and there, they tucked into their night stands. Now I understood why I had seen so many cockroaches scuttling under the patients' beds when I served the trays. With all that food in the ward, it would be impossible to keep pests out.

But I didn't really mind about the cockroaches. I was glad to see that some of those sad-faced men had someone who had not forgotten them. Someone who knew their names.

After I got my coat and purse from the locker room, I stood a moment at the door of the hospital before I went out onto the street. I had the scissors in my coat pocket, and my hand closed over them, ready. I peered through the door. There was no one waiting on the steps. It was still light enough to see down the street to the bus stop. I didn't see the big, tough aide anywhere. But I wasn't sure I wanted to be seen standing alone, waiting for the bus. I decided to walk on to the next stop and board it there.

I had walked no more than a block before I was sorry. The hospital bus stop was directly across the street from a well-lighted business block. Past that, dusk closed in around me as only an occasional street light pierced the ghetto gloom. A skinny dog growled at me, then scuttled under a broken fence, escaping the expected kick. A few figures perched on the outside stoops of rickety frame buildings watched me silently. My own steps sounded loud as cannons in the quiet street. I peered uneasily ahead, looking for the stop sign, reminding myself that doctors and nurses in white are rarely attacked by a community dependent on their mercy. But how about aides in blue?

Then I found the next bus sign, and waited no more than ten minutes before the bus appeared. I climbed on, grabbed a strap with a sigh of relief, and let the crush of bodies next to me bear my own weight. I had left the hospital that night bone-weary, depressed and frightened, and now I wondered if I would have the courage to go back.

But there was something in those nameless patients' blank, sick eyes that drew me back the following morning.

CHAPTER *THREE*

Patients Live
and Dead

I kept Teddy's scissors for three days but I never found my enemy lying in wait for me outside, and when I did see her in the corridor at the hospital, she looked right past me as though there was nothing going between us, so I finally stopped sweating and gave the scissors back to Teddy.

During my first week of work I didn't get much closer to any patient than handing him a tray of food, but by the time the week was over I was beginning to get better organized in my job so that I found I had a little time to spare between breakfast and lunch. The way that Kilpatrick flew around the floor I knew she could use more help. She was the only RN to cover the eighty-bed ward. Her staff consisted of me and two male aides, Teddy and a slightly built, good looking young Negro war veteran named Lester.

The beginning of my second week I asked Kilpatrick if I could do anything for her when I had a spare moment.

She looked me up and down, hands on the place where her hips should have been, and then she smiled. It was one of those broad, shining smiles that can make a plain face beautiful.

"Do you know how to take a temperature?"

"Yes," I told her. "I learned that in high school."

"Can you make a bed?"

"Sure thing," I nodded. While I had not yet tried to make a hospital bed, I had watched the way the aides stretched the sheets taut, envelope fashion, or fan-folded the covers to receive patients from surgery.

"Did you ever do a PM?"

I looked blank.

"Post-mortem," Kilpatrick translated swiftly. "If you're scared of bodies, forget it. If not, I'll show you how it's done. We could certainly use another hand with the PMs. They stack up fast some days and I don't like leaving them around with the other patients —they're depressed enough as it is."

For all her abrupt manner, I had already learned that Kilpatrick, unlike many of the RNs at the hospital, had compassion for her patients. She might not know their names, either, but she did care how they felt, and she did what she could for them.

The time had not yet arrived when most of the RNs refused to touch patients, as many of them do at

40

the hospital today, but the trend was in the air. The senior nurses were already serving as supervisors rather than giving bedside patient care. Practical nurses were being trained to do the work RNs had once done. And the patients saw more of the nurse's aides than they did anyone else. Their comfort depended on them. I have seen an RN walk by a patient who is in real distress and who begs her for a bedpan, and if that patient is lower class or black she will stand there and scream for an aide to come take care of him. If the aide can't come at once, the nurse will walk on to her desk rather than fetch it herself, leaving the unfortunate patient to suffer the humiliation of the inevitable "accident."

The same thing is true if the patient has finished using the bedpan and calls to a passing RN to "please take this away." That can be a real tragedy—to ask an RN to remove a bedpan—even though keeping it in bed with him may make an already ill patient nauseous. But there aren't many Florence Nightingales left around city hospitals any more. The only time you see RNs giving bedside care today is if we have a bigshot patient. Then she will insist on personally caring for him. If he's not too sick, that is.

Kilpatrick was a shining exception to that trend in nursing. She was a good nurse who cared about her patients and who didn't give a damn about hierarchy or status. She could be counted on to stand up for the patient and she wasn't afraid of the devil. One time I overheard her tell a pompous chief of staff who was criticizing her that he could, with her permission, go shit in his hat. She made this observation, then walked off and left him standing there with his mouth open, while she went on with her work. She wasn't fired for that incident, which I feared she would be, but I'm sure that's one of the reasons that she is still a floor nurse today and never was made a supervisor.

Her patients loved her—except when she came around with a needle. Wherever Kilpatrick had trained, they had neglected to teach her how to give an injection properly. She had only one idea: get the needle in and out of the flesh as quickly as possible and go on to the next patient. She would go down a line of beds, seizing a piece of patient flesh at random, while talking over her shoulder to one of the aides at the same time, harpoon the flash with her needle as a veterinarian might a horse, without making any effort to "spread" the muscle to ease the pain, simply jam in the needle, spill out its contents, then proceed to the next patient.

"You killed me! You killed me!" the patient would scream. But Kilpatrick never looked back. She was a good city nurse. She never heard a cry.

I started taking temperatures and helping make the beds that same day. At once, the patients began to come into focus as individual people for me. Not just mouths to feed or charts to read or individual diseases, but personalities.

There was one man in particular who caught my attention. He had been brought in and dumped into a

corner bed of one of the larger rooms several days
after I started to work and he was by all odds the
worst looking patient on the floor. A Negro wino,
drifter or derelict, he was obviously suffering from
malnutrition as well as whatever disease had brought
him to the hospital (I think it was a cardiac condition) so that, while he was probably not more than
fifty-five or sixty years old, he looked, in his dried-out,
wrinkled fleshlessness, as ancient as our most elderly
patients. He had not shaved in several days before he
came to the hospital and he had a black stubble of
beard when he arrived. Each day it grew longer. Wiry
and tough, the black hair shot out in various directions.
The untrimmed beard irritated his skin, so that as it
grew, the skin beneath began to erupt in angry, red
pimples. By the time I was embarking on patient care,
taking temperatures and making beds, this man's
beard had grown to nearly four inches in length.

He was such a miserable-looking creature that no
one paid any attention to him, neither staff nor the
other patients. He never spoke to anyone, but just lay
there, thin, silent, black and ugly, in his bed in the
corner of the room. At visiting hours I looked in on the
ward and saw that no one came to visit him. He was
so obviously the underdog of the entire floor that I
made up my mind, when I found time, to pay special
attention to him. I looked up his chart and found
that he was listed as Smith.

In those days the hospital did not have a regular
barber service which automatically cared for all male

patients as they do today. There was a barber who put in an occasional appearance but he was on strict orders and he had a trick of only shaving those patients who could pay him, or whose families saw to it that he was tipped for his service. Obviously, he did not go near my derelict patient since there was nothing in it for him.

When I first approached this patient to take his temperature, I said, "Good morning, Mr. Smith." He made no reply. He did glance up at me but his eyes showed no flicker of reaction. Like so many drifters, he had apparently long since outlived communication with other human beings. He had no family, no friends. He was simply existing until that time when he would be transformed from an ill, but still live, body into a dead one to be carted off to the morgue.

The second time I came to take his temperature, I again greeted him, and then pointed to his hideous beard—which looked more suitable for some wild animal than for a man. "Would you like to have me shave it off?" I asked him.

His flat, dark glance flickered briefly, and he nodded that he would. I think he had forgotten how to speak.

Kilpatrick found a safety razor and a blade for me to use but when I went hunting for shaving cream I could not find any. I had seen the aide, Lester, shave a patient, but when I asked him for shaving cream, he told me that he was not free to lend it to me since it had been bought by the family of the man he shaved.

44

Patients Live and Dead

I settled for plain soap. But when I took my tray of
supplies: soap, razor, hot water and towels, to the
ward and started to work on my patient, I quickly
discovered that this was no one-time job. I could not
possibly use the razor until I had got the beard
trimmed down close to the face. I soaked it with hot
towels, then got Teddy's scissors and started working
on it. As I worked I noticed that a number of the
other men in the ward were watching with considerable interest. I was only twenty years old and had not
yet put on any weight, and had quite a good figure,
so I guess the sight of me bouncing around playing
barber was the best show they had had in some time.

I had to clip the beard three times to get it short
enough so that I could use the razor to give my patient
a clean shave. The morning that I scraped off the last
of the beard, the men in the ward all sat up in their
beds and clapped their hands, applauding me. They
seemed very pleased with the performance, including
my little old derelict patient himself, who sat there,
happily stroking his clean cheek with his hand. One
of the other patients volunteered some healing lotion
to help clean up the irritated skin. I patted that on,
whisked off the towel I had draped around his neck,
and packed up my tray of supplies.

Then I heard a funny little squeaky sound, like an
unused bolt being slipped back from a door.

"Thank you," he said.

They were the first words I had heard him utter.
As I picked up my tray and started out of the room

45

to get back to my duties in the kitchen, several of the men plucked at my skirt as I went by their beds. "Shave me tomorrow?" they clamored. "And me?"

They all wanted to be shaved. I promised several of the men, whom I had seen had no family to help them, that I would try to get around to shaving them too. But I refused to help the men who had someone else to do it for them. To shave the entire ward would have been an eight-hour job.

When the word spread over the floor that I had begun shaving some of the patients for free each day, the other aides all laughed at me and told me what a hopeless square I was, to do that extra work for nothing. But it wasn't nothing to me. I felt better the day I got my little man shaved than I had since I went to work at the hospital.

Besides my little old men, another person at the hospital soon sized me up for a willing patsy. I was standing outside my kitchen, waiting for my first twenty patients to finish using their plates and forks at lunch, when a short, skinny, dark, hungry looking little intern cruised past. When I smiled and said good morning, he skidded to a halt in front of me (they always seemed to be on the run), his nose in the air, sniffing eagerly, and started to chat. The way he sniffed the odors from the food truck in the kitchen, I knew what had made him stop and get acquainted. I had all that food going for me and I was worth cultivating.

He started in telling me about how poor he was

(he looked it, with a haircut that must have been done under a bowl, and both soles of his shoes half off), but I was so poor myself I couldn't think of a less interesting subject.

"I've been through all that, too," I cut him off.

Then he hurried up and got to the point. His parents were sending him through medical school but they didn't have enough money to provide a lunch allowance and interns had to pay for what they ate.

"Don't you worry about a thing, baby," I told him. "Come here every day about this time and I'll fix you up with something."

I made up my mind that with all those nurses raiding the food, I could certainly manage to hold out enough to feed one skinny little doctor.

Out of my first twenty patients that I had served that day, two had been too ill to want their trays, so I put together a good lunch for him.

After that the little intern—his name was Dr. Porto —turned up every day. He had not, I found, given me any snow job about being poor. His parents were second generation Italians who lived on the edge of the black ghetto, not far from the hospital, and it took every nickel they could scrape together to keep him in medical school.

The next morning I saw Dr. Porto climb on my bus as I was going to work. He saw me too, gave me a big wave and came over and sat down. After that, we had a little visit most every morning on the way to work, and became good friends. Between me and another kitchen aide we fed him through his internship and residency.

One day we had an especially low census, I guess because it was summertime and not many people were sick, so that even after the staff raided the food truck, and I had fed my patients and Dr. Porto, there was still nearly a half a container full of turkey and gravy. I was cleaning up the lunch dishes when Kilpatrick dropped by the kitchen, and her eyes lighted on the turkey. She handed me an empty two-pound coffee can. "Fill that up before they come to take the truck away," she told me, "and take the turkey home to your kids. It'll save your having to cook tonight."

I hesitated, thinking how angry I had been at the way the staff stole the patients' food. "I don't want to take hospital food," I protested.

"Maybe not every day," Kilpatrick agreed. "But you'd be a fool not to take this today, when no one needs it. It'll just go to waste."

I decided that made sense, so I filled the can with turkey and gravy, and took it home with me that night. I was heating it in a double boiler for the boys' supper, when my brother Jim came into the kitchen to say goodbye before he left for work.

"What's that stuff?" he asked suspiciously. He knew I hadn't been home long enough to cook turkey.

"Turkey," I said.

"From the hospital?" he asked, his eyes narrowing with anger.

I nodded. "They had a lot left over today."

By now I was dishing up the plates for the boys who were already sitting at the table waiting. As I set the plates before them, Jim pointed a long black finger at the drumsticks that I had picked out for them, and said,

"Do you know what that is? That's patients' legs!"

Both the little boys shrieked and threw down their forks and pushed the plates away. "Don't make us eat it, Mama!" Billy yelled.

"Now what made you go and do that?" I grumbled at my brother. I was really pretty sore about all that good food going to waste, and me having to cook something else.

"I'll tell you why." Jim towered over me, and right then he reminded me of my Daddy when he was about to go into a sermon. "Because I never want you to bring hospital food into this house again—you hear? If you don't have the money to buy food for the kids, tell me, and if I don't have it, I'll borrow it from a friend. But you keep that city stuff out of this house. Understand?"

"Yes, Jim." I hung my head just as if he really was my Daddy. Because I knew he was right. I hadn't wanted to take the food in the first place. I never did it again.

By now I had been North long enough that I was beginning to make some friends on my own, outside of my family. There was a pair of sisters that shared an apartment in the building next door to us that I saw a lot of. Clarice and Loula were both divorcees

49

with two small children each and they were very poor, but they were good looking women who managed to look well dressed, and they were fun to be with. The building they lived in was not in as good condition as ours, and their apartment was much smaller and more cramped. The two women and four children were packed together in two and a half rooms—there was only one small bedroom, a living room and a tiny, windowless kitchen. The women slept in the bedroom and the four kids shared the two small sofas in the living room at night. The sisters took turn about, with part-time jobs at the hospital or wherever else they could find work in the area, one working while the other watched the kids. They managed to feed the kids but it was a rice and beans diet and whenever I had a little extra meat I gave it to them.

Clarice, especially, attracted me. She was a warm, noisy, droll sort of woman who had a way of rolling her eyes that could always make me laugh. She also seemed to be very religious and loved to sing, and I really thought I had found myself a soul sister. Clarice and Loula took me with them to their church —the one where all the poor parishioners had to contribute their "pound" of food each month—and while I didn't think much of the preacher—he was entirely too sporty for me to believe his sermons about the ways of the meek and the righteous—I did love the music.

Clarice and I used to sing together sometimes outside of church. One night she came to visit in my kitchen and I was feeling pretty blue. My job paid sixty-two dollars every two weeks and sometimes that sixty-two dollars just didn't stretch to cover everything the boys and I needed. Some unexpected expense would come up, and I'd find I had an empty purse the last few days before payday. This particular evening I had managed to give the children supper but we were out of soap, and I didn't have any to bathe them, and for some reason that unattainable bar of soap depressed me. Judson hadn't been contributing anything to our support—although I kept hoping that when he did finally show up he'd bring some money with him—but knowing him, I doubted it.

Anyhow, I was feeling miserable about not being able to bathe my children, and Clarice was poorer than I was, so she couldn't help me any. So we just talked a while to bring up my morale a little and then we got to humming and finally we just broke out singing like we did in church. It felt so good we kept it up and around midnight I suddenly heard steps in the hall. Our building was locked so it had to be someone with a key, and sure enough I heard the key in the lock and my brother Jim walked in carrying a big carton.

He set it down in the middle of the table and started pulling stuff out. There was a ham and a turkey, and a pound of butter, and a pound of coffee and a dozen eggs and a cake and several loaves of bread. There wasn't a bar of soap, but I didn't mind.

"One of my customers at the garage gave me all

this," he explained. "They had a big buffet party last night and they are leaving for Florida today, so they decided to clean out their refrigerator before they left."

"See, see, Louanne!" Clarice was so excited her eyes were rolling and she swayed like she was going to fall (right into my brother, I should have noticed. I found out later, every time she stands near a handsome man she faints). "The Lord answered you!"

"Jim, not the Lord," I corrected her. I could always count on Jim. I took the food and divided it into two piles and gave her one. After all, she had sung just as loud as I had.

After that, Clarice really hung around my kitchen. I guess she hadn't got a close look at my brother Jim before—or else she was fresh out of a lover. She really worked on him. Pretty soon he started taking her out. Which was all right with me because Jim was old enough to take care of himself, and besides I hadn't really caught on to her yet myself.

So far, I wasn't going out with men. Judson had been mustered out of service, but instead of coming straight to us he had gone home to Alabama to be with one of his sisters who was ill. When anyone in his own family needed him, there was no question about where he would go. Despite the long separation, however, I still had hopes of working out our marriage —provided he would ever come home. There were several of the male aides at the hospital who had been giving me the eye—especially Lester—and I did like his looks, but there was something about him that made me uneasy, although I couldn't pin down just what it was. He wasn't as kind-hearted as Teddy, but he was a quick, graceful man, and I liked to work with him at the hospital.

The next time that we had a death on the ward, Kilpatrick called me to help her prepare the body for the morgue. After the doctor had pronounced the death, we screened the bed off at one side of the ward, then she brought out the Post-mortem pack and showed me how to put it on the body. I found I was so busy following her instructions and studying the deft way she handled the body, that the procedure did not affect me as badly as I had feared it might.

Besides, the whole thing makes sense. The body is wrapped with gauze padding, placed so that it protects the face from being bruised, and keeps the limbs in place so that they don't fall when the body is being moved; and the orifices are covered to protect against possible drainage. Then the body is wrapped and tied into a shroud, leaving an outer identification tag visible on one toe. The procedure is best done by two people since the body must be supported on its side while the padding is placed and tied, but in a hospital as busy as ours, with so many deaths, it is often done by one experienced attendant.

I assisted Kilpatrick with Post-mortems until she was satisfied that I had learned the technique correctly, and then she had me work with the aides. One afternoon, I was assisting her when Teddy came and summoned her to another room for an emergency resuscitation.

"See if you can do it alone," she called to me as she ran out to get the respirator.

We had just got the Morgue pack unwrapped and set out, but as yet had done nothing with the body. I got the pads tied in place, then stretched out the shroud and attempted to roll the body into it. Then I realized the only way I could get it secured properly in the back was to balance the body on the very edge of the bed so that it rested against my body, while I bent over and worked on the ties in back. I had the corpse balanced against my chest, and was straining over it, tying the back ties, when the body suddenly let out a long sigh, "Whooosh!"

I stopped, paralyzed with fear, my hands in the air, waiting for him next to speak to me.

The sweat broke out on my forehead and in the palms of my hands. But I just stood there, rooted to the spot. If I moved the body would roll off the bed onto the floor. Terrified as I was I knew enough to remember that there would be hell to pay if I dropped him. Although public hospitals are not subject to nearly the number of lawsuits that private hospitals are, Kilpatrick had warned me that if you batter up or bruise the face of a dearly beloved—you're in trouble if he's got any kinfolks at all.

I just stood where I was for a few long moments, frozen. Then, when he didn't say anything, nor sigh a second time, I began to get control of myself. I looked down at the wrapped body which was still balanced against my chest. There was no movement, no life, no breath. I tried to reconstruct what had happened. I have always had an ample bosom, even in those days when I was relatively thin, and I figured that when I was straining across the body, my breast probably pushed so hard into the abdomen that if there was a little air in there, it was pushed upward into—and out of—the mouth. That's all that sigh amounted to. He was dead, I told myself; even if he had had that little bit of air left inside of him. I forced myself to reach over, finish tying the shroud, and then, very slowly and carefully, I eased the body back over till it once again rested on its back on the bed. Then I looked at it a moment, just to be sure. The body was still, swathed, silent. Yes, he was dead.

I went out to the corridor to find a stretcher and get someone to help remove the body to the morgue. Kilpatrick hadn't reappeared but I knew she'd appreciate it if we'd get the body off her floor before more patients saw it. I found Lester and asked his help and we loaded the corpse onto a stretcher and started for the morgue.

I had never been down to the morgue before and I figured it was time I learned how to get there. One afternoon we had had three deaths on our floor, and Kilpatrick told me there were always more patients who died at night. Occasionally the morgue had such a stack-up of corpses that they sent up word to hold

55

the bodies till they could make room below—and we had to have them lying around the corridors. Once when a state senator came around to investigate, there was a corpse in a wheelchair that had been there for an entire day—without even getting shrouded.

We took the stretcher down in the elevator to the subbasement of the main building. When we rolled it off, I looked uneasily down the dimly lit corridor. There were no guards on duty down there in those days, and the block long corridor was narrow, dark, hardly more than an alleyway, with only two tiny light bulbs, one at the elevator landing and the other down at the door of the morgue. The morgue itself was a small, square brick icebox of a room not much larger than the furnace room of a private house. Inside it was lined with drawers where the bodies were stacked like cordwood until they were claimed by the families or could be disposed of. Since the body is not tied to the stretcher it usually takes two people to ease it off onto one of those drawers without its rolling off onto the floor. Later, after Sis joined me at the hospital, she often did the whole job alone. But she always did have more nerve than I.

When we had deposited the body, I asked Lester about the corridor. "Where does it go from here?"

"There's nothing down here on this floor," he told me, "except the morgue and the heating plant and—" he grinned "—the 'office' in the back of the furnace room where the night guard Ollie takes bets—"

"Numbers, baby, numbers," he laughed at my blank face. "Don't tell me you never bought a digit?"

As a matter of fact I had had my own private brush with numbers but I wasn't about to let him know it. I hadn't realized it was a hospital game.

"I thought you could get through underground to the other buildings." I shifted the subject to safer ground.

"You can—one floor up. Want to see it?"

"Yes." I decided if I was this far into the bowels of the hospital I might as well get the whole scene. Patients were frequently transported, via the underground passage, from one building to another and I might very well be called upon to accompany one, so I should know the way.

We took the elevator up one flight and started out into the passageway that led from the main building over to the neurosurgical building. This corridor was considerably wider than the dark alley below, and it was well lighted. It was also busy. Nurse's aides and doctors were scurrying past, some pushing patients in wheelchairs, others assisting ambulatory patients.

"Bend your head down while we get past this part," Lester told me. "It's easier to breathe."

Directly before us rose a cloud of wet steam so thick that the figures scurrying past us momentarily disappeared, then were visible again a few yards beyond. I had several of the patients gasp and cough inside the wet cloud.

"What on earth is it?"

"Hell, honey," he laughed. "If we can't cure 'em, we just cook 'em. Take a big breath and go through fast."

I did as he told me, holding my breath as I entered the sheet of steam. Once, before I reached the other side, I took a quick breath—and the hot air scalded my lungs. It must have been 120 degrees. When I reached the other side of the steamy curtain I stopped to mop my face.

"What causes it?"

"Some faulty pipes, I guess," Lester shrugged. "Whatever it is, they don't seem to be able to get it fixed. It's been that way as long as I've worked here —going on two years now."

I wondered how the patients, weak as they were, could stand it. Today, I still wonder. Nearly a quarter of a century later we are still, as Lester said, "cooking" our patients when we take them from one building to another.

My concern about the patients did not endear me to most of the other hospital workers. With no strong and positive direction from the top, their morale was zero. Short-handed as we were, I had noticed that whenever a worker was not under specific orders, rather than look around for something that needed to be done, he or she was very apt to be found catching a smoke in the lavatory or hiding out in a supply room with a cup of coffee. At least I thought it was coffee when I first watched them. Then I happened to get a whiff of one of those paper cups one day and I asked one of the aides, a young Negro girl named Jennie who worked on the other side of the floor, about it.

"Coffee, you kidding?" she chuckled. "Honey, you really are a square! That's booze, baby. Want some?"

"No." I felt suddenly awkward—as though I'd just caught somebody shoplifting and didn't want them to know I'd seen it.

"And you know what that is?" She pointed to the big sister who had threatened me, who was leaning against the stairwell, smoking. "That ain't tobacco either, baby, that's a reefer."

Now I was shocked. Not at the idea of drugs—at the idea of handling sick people when you were on drugs. I guess I must have showed what I was thinking, because she laid her hand on my arm, and her voice was hard.

"Now don't you go feeling superior!" she warned me. "If you don't take a drink or a drug now and then, you aren't going to last around here—understand?" Then her face suddenly went slack and sad. "All these smells, all this death and sadness—" she gestured helplessly toward the ward nearest us, "—if you don't take something, baby, it'll drive you crazy after a while!"

CHAPTER *FOUR*

The Little
Old Crocks

Once Kilpatrick discovered that I not only would help her out, but that I liked to work with the patients, she gave me as much patient care as she could, although it was illegal, and she also assigned Teddy to assist me with the diet duties. Teddy and I soon had the meal service worked down to a fast routine. We'd pass out our twenty plates and forks, then get a sinkful of hot sudsy water started in the kitchen sink and race back and forth picking up the plates and forks in the ward as fast as the patients were finished, dunk them in the hot water, then shake them dry as we walked from sink to food truck, and load them up again. In this fashion we could serve our patient load—which ranged from sixty to eighty men—in two hours. That left me a couple of hours free for patient care between breakfast and lunch; another hour between lunch and the end of my shift.

Now that I had been handing out trays for several weeks, I had a number of our patients sorted out in my mind, although our census changed each day, as some died, some were discharged, and strangers filled their beds. There was one slender young Negro veteran named Jenner who had caught my eye—mainly because he was so anti-social. He kept his face to the wall, and never spoke to any of the other patients. Most of the time, when I went to pick up his tray, the food was untouched.

Then there was a handsome, elderly Irishman with faded, sweet blue eyes who asked me to call him Tom, and always thanked me for his food in a very courtly fashion. And of course there was my shaved friend, Mr. Smith, who by now had progressed so far that he could actually say "Good morning" and "Thank you." There was also another elderly Negro man, Bullett, who had replaced Smith in my affections because he was even worse off than Smith had been. So terribly crippled he couldn't sit up, he was shaped like a skinny little black pretzel, all curls and painful angles where he should have been straight.

The first morning that Kilpatrick assigned me to make beds, I went into the large room where so many of these patients that I knew were, smiled "Good morning," and went over to the first bed which happened to be that of my old Irish friend, Tom. By now I knew Tom quite well. I had been giving him his breakfast and lunch for days; I had handed out mail to him; rubbed his back when he was feeling achy. But when I threw back the covers, I was speechless with shock.

Tom was a cardiac patient. Apparently, however, he had been operated on for rectal cancer at an earlier time. And no one in the hospital had been taking proper care of him. The colostomy bag that he wore, which was supposed to catch any evacuation, had not been properly cleaned lately and it was not fitted properly. Only a little of the most recent bowel movement had been caught by the bag. The rest of it had run all over his stomach, onto the sheets and was dripping down the sides of the bed. It was the first colostomy case I had seen. And I didn't know where to begin to clean it.

"Just a minute, Tom." I tried to keep the horror out of my voice, as I laid the sheet gently back up over him. I got a screen and set it up around the bed, then went to call Kilpatrick.

"I never saw a patient who had a bowel movement through his stomach before," I told her. "I don't know what to do!"

"Just don't get sick!" Kilpatrick snorted. Then her voice was serious. "You are not supposed to use gloves when you work on a patient, because then the patient feels that you think he is too dirty to touch. But, since this is your first time, wear rubber gloves. Talk to him nicely, and maybe he won't notice. But try to relax, Louanne. Think what it's like to be in his place."

Then she told me how to clean and air the bag properly, how to adjust a temporary gauze bandage so that it would not irritate the tender flesh. "Good luck," she said as she hurried off.

I got the supplies I needed and walked slowly back to the ward. The thought of the mess awaiting me nearly turned my stomach. But then I thought of Tom. He wasn't just a sick old body to me. He was a dear man with a sweet smile and a wonderful face. A man I liked—and respected. Now, I realized, it was my job to show him that I still respected him—despite the humiliation of this terrible disease.

He looked up at me—his blue eyes guarded—as I walked to his bed.

"I had to get some gauze and tape, Tom," I smiled. "I didn't mean to keep you waiting."

He returned my smile—faintly—but said nothing. As I worked I suddenly felt ashamed of the gloves I wore. His body wasn't a horror. It was part of him. A sick part, as any of us might have, anytime. I peeked at him, and saw the proud bright color in his cheeks. How humiliating it must be to feel like nothing but a mass of flesh—when you still have a sense of your own worth and identity. Yet the victim has no choice.

Suddenly I was angry. Not at Tom. Nor even myself. But at the tragedy of it—that someone like him who needed such special, kindly care was at the mercy of an untrained girl like me. Whether I was kind—or cruel—was just his luck. I wasn't cruel, but my first impulse had been to get the hell out of there and never have to face such an unsightly scene again. And I almost did—except that I also had realized how much he needed me. I wasn't trained. I wasn't equipped medically or psychologically to handle him. But who else did he have to turn to? I felt like a prize fighter who gets that knockout blow in the gut—but then, somehow, knows he must rally and go on.

As I finished tying the gauze bandage in place I deliberately worked very slowly, then looked into his face and smiled.

"You don't seem to mind doing this, Miss Ferris," Tom said softly, a wistful thread of hope in his voice. "It's hard to get most of the aides to stay long enough to do the job right—"

"No," I said, blinking back the mist of tears as I realized how neglected he had been (and never complained), "I don't mind. Honest."

Tom asked for me each day after that. And I gave him his care each morning. I never wore the gloves again. Nor did I feel the need of them. The trick, I realized, was to think about the patient, the person he was, instead of thinking about yourself and how you don't like to dirty your hands. Our patients—old, sick, abandoned, dying—could be any one of us, anytime.

The worst thing about giving the patients their morning care, I found, was the lack of supplies. We were short of toothbrushes, combs, soap, towels. The mouthwash solution was made up in a wooden vat, and stirred with a big wooden paddle, and it often had little splinters of wood in it. There were never

64

enough pillows, pillow cases or sheets to go around. Those of us who were determined to give the best care we could to our patients got in the habit of locking up or hiding the linen so that we would have it to use on our own shifts. Sometimes the patients helped us—they'd sneak a sheet or pillow case into their night stand so that they could look forward to having their bed changed the next day.

There were no washcloths. The aides made their own from old sheets. I don't know what material those sheets had been made from, but instead of getting soft with age, as linen or a good muslin does, they got brittle, like wood. The backsides of the older patients were often badly irritated, and it seemed criminal to wash that raw, red, skin with those harsh cloths.

It's amazing how quickly the skin can deteriorate when a person stays in bed and is not turned frequently. On our elderly patients the skin often begins to break down and bedsores develop within only three or four days' hospitalization. The sores crop up wherever friction points exist: on the buttocks, the elbows, even the backs of the shoulders. I've heard many nurses claim bed sores cannot be cured. But they can. The essential ingredient for curing bed sores is conscientious nursing care. The patient must be turned frequently, and the sores treated to encourage the regrowth of tissue and skin. The area also should be regularly massaged to stimulate the circulation. The routine hospital medication is A&D ointment but I found brown soap more healing.

When an aide gives a patient a bedpan and he screams, it often is because the dressing was pushed off a bedsore. They also scream if the bedpan is "boiling" hot, from the sterilizer, or if it's freezing cold. When I could take the time to do it I rubbed the bedpan with the bedcover before putting the patient on it so it approximated bed temperature. Sometimes when the senile patients became enraged with the treatment they received from the aides, they took their feces and threw it at them. This was also true in the psycho ward, where the aides are in constant threat of getting a plop of feces in the middle of their backs.

One of the worst offenses against adequate patient care in the wards was the condition of the linen rooms and the bedpan flushers. The dirty linen bags and chutes were always encrusted with fecal material and blood; the bedpan flushers failed to work about half of the time with the result that the pans had to be mopped out by hand—not only a filthy job for whoever had to do it, but completely nonsterile so far as the patient was concerned.

On days when we were especially short-staffed, and those of us on duty were simply unable to get around to all the patients when they needed us, feces seemed to lie in wait wherever we turned. As my outspoken, fiery little friend Lettie, who worked in Male Surgery, put it, "Before you can give a patient breakfast you got to wash the shit off *his* hands. Before you can get yourself a cup of coffee you got to wash the shit off *your* hands. Your hands smell like shit all day long!"

I was still feeling pretty good about my victory over my own squeamishness with Tom, when Teddy and I finished serving lunch and Kilpatrick asked me to check on a couple of patients who had just been sent to us from the surgical floor.

"What am I supposed to check?" I whispered.

"Oh, just see if they look all right," she said nonchalantly. "If anything's wrong call me. I'll be in Room Eight giving medication to the asthma patient."

Our asthma patient, Big Joe, was a darling whom Kilpatrick and I were both fond of—a tall, handsome, soft-voiced black man of about fifty, with a gentle way about him who never gave us any trouble. We all knew him well since he was ambulatory and often walked out to the desk or the kitchen to chat with us.

I walked into the ward where the new surgical patients were, wondering just what it was I was supposed to do. They were both awake. The first one greeted me wanly, and when I asked if there was anything I could do, shook his head and closed his eyes. Since he obviously was alive, breathing, and simply wanted to sleep, I left him alone. The second one was alert, and apparently upset about something.

"Nurse, nurse—" his voice was weak and thready. "Would you look and see what's wrong? I feel wet—"

Wet sounded like urine to me, so I casually flipped back the sheet expecting to find it soaked. It was. But not with urine. With blood. The surgical incision had come open—and the coiled length of the patient's intestine had bubbled up out of the wound and now lay in a heap on top of his belly.

I felt my knees buckle, and grasped the edge of the bed for support. For one awful moment I was afraid I was going down, but I hung on, prayed, and the moment passed.

I glanced quickly at the patient's face. He was lying with his head back against the pillow and he had obviously not seen what I saw. I carefully laid the sheet back over his body—up to his chin—and said, as calmly as I could manage, "I'll call someone."

I walked out the door, then once I hit the corridor I started running. I located Kilpatrick. She paged a surgeon. We wheeled the patient back to the operating room. In another hour he had been sewed up again, and was still very much alive.

"Wound disruption," as this particularly ghastly phenomenon is commonly called, is not so rare as one might think, and also, happily, is rarely fatal. It happens to obese patients, or patients who get a coughing fit soon after surgery, or who simply are the unfortunate victims of indifferent surgeons who, like bad dressmakers, suture sloppily.

A frequent and sadder sight common to the city hospital (because we have so many diabetic and aged patients) is ulcerated legs. Several time I turned back the covers and found the patient's leg half eaten away by the lesions that were slowly destroying the tissue and the discharge all over the bed. This is the sort of sight which makes you just start to cry and walk away.

The more I worked close to the patients, however, the more I found that I could do for them. Even hopeless cases could be made more comfortable. The cancer patient, the ulcerated patient, can be cleaned up temporarily. They can be shaved. It made me angry at first to see how utterly untended many of them were. Fingernails and toenails were two and three inches long, so that they curled back and cut the flesh.

Whatever time I had free, I found myself cutting, cleaning, shining, oiling my patients. And how they loved the attention! When I walked by their beds, they would reach out and grab my hand and kiss it, and often try to kiss my face when I bent over them. Many of the men automatically reached out and patted the female aides' backsides as they walked by. Some of the girls resented this but I didn't. The patients who did that were usually the oldest and loneliest—for whom any human contact could transform an hour or a day. One of the loneliest men in our ward was an ancient Jewish gentleman, Sol, who would catch my hand and kiss it whenever I spoke to him. Sometimes I found him in tears. Usually our Jewish patients had family to visit them but poor old Sol must have outlived every last one of his relatives because no one ever came to see him and he was a man who sadly needed affection.

As I found my way from one bed to the next, one tragedy to the next, I began to feel more compassion for the aides who had a secret drink in the supply room, or smoked a reefer in the stairwell before they faced such duties. A few of these cases and any normal person felt the need of a stiff drink. I was beginning to realize that in hospital work there are several ways one can go: one became as callous as the nursing supervisor who could stare out of her window each day at the human tissue on the fence spikes and be unmoved by the sight, or one could stay half drunk or doped up on the job so as not to see or feel anything too clearly—as some of the aides did. Or one could go the Kilpatrick route: a survival shell of toughness tempered with compassion, and the overriding belief that there was something that could—and should —be done. She was my girl.

Except for the elderly patients who lived at the hospital until they were removed to a nursing home or died, most of the patients were transients—strangers who appeared for a few days, died or recovered, then disappeared, their beds immediately taken by others. Each day when I made beds, I found some new patients. Important information about the patients is supposed to be posted on the foot of the bed.

In some of the city hospitals, even the patient's religious preference is posted on his bed—red, blue and green for Protestant, Catholic and Jew, so that the priest or rabbi or minister can spot "his" patients the moment he enters a crowded ward. They even have a white card for "Other." At the time we were most crowded, beds spilled out into the corridors, where the patients had to be bathed and bedpanned on public display. And the intravenous stands stood around like leafless winter trees, to be ducked as one hurried by, like making one's way through a jungle.

The third day I was giving morning care, Kilpatrick assigned me to make the bed of a new patient, and as I wound the bed down to the flat position, then loosened the bedding from the bottom, preparatory to changing it, I happened to glance up at the head of the bed and, to my horror, I saw the man's face was turning blue.

I ran for Kilpatrick. By the time we got back to him, the patient was dead.

"He was a coronary," she explained. "There should have been a note on his bed that he had to be kept elevated at all times." She hurried on out to the desk to call a doctor to pronounce death.

I felt sick. I thought I had killed him. No one blamed me for the accident. But no one consoled me either. It was a routine event for Kilpatrick and the rest of the staff. They thought nothing more about it. I guess none of them realized how terrible I felt. I called in sick for two days and stayed home and prayed. Then finally I realized there was nothing I could do to bring the man back to life. There was no point in torturing myself any longer. It was the first time I had contributed to a patient's death. And if I stayed at the hospital I knew it might not be the last. I had seen patients die each day, from nursing error, doctor error, medication error, and plain neglect, as well as from "natural causes"—although that's what was usually written down on the medical report. I went back to work.

Our patients in those days were about fifty-fifty

black and white. What they had in common was the overriding poverty that kept them all in the same slum neighborhood. The hospital workers also were drawn from the same area, and were, in fact the same as the patients, half and half, black and white. A third were men. While male aides are essential to a hospital, I felt that the women were more apt (despite their constant grumbling) to prove compassionate to the patients. Teddy was a well-meaning, kindly man and did what he could for everyone. Lester did what he had to quite efficiently, but then goofed off some of the time. There were other men who did just as little as possible. They were the ones you caught sneaking a smoke or booze in the linen closets or stairwells, or sleeping off a hangover on a stretcher or an unoccupied bed. There was one callous young man named Duke whom I had seen working on the other side of our floor, who really got my dander up. He just didn't give a good goddam about any patient. Twice in one week I knew that he took patients to X-ray—and abandoned them there. Then when a nurse found the patient had been sitting around for three hours instead of having been taken back to the ward she sent out the alarm—and our boy was found in the bar across the street getting a quick one. Why the hospital didn't fire him I don't know.

I was taking temperatures in our ward a few mornings later, when Duke came in with orders to take our crippled patient, Bullett, to the bathroom for a bath.

"Be careful," I called after him, "he can't support himself."

A few minutes later, I walked past the bathroom. Duke had got Mr. Bullett into the tub, but there were no handrails on the front of the tub.

"You better set up a restraint, so he'll have something that he can hang onto," I cautioned.

Duke gave me a nasty look. "And why don't you mind your own damn business?" he asked.

I turned around and walked on. Bullett was his patient, not mine. But I was worried about Duke's attitude toward him. One time I had tried to get Mr. Bullett into a chair but I had found it was impossible for him to sit up unaided.

When Teddy and I started to serve lunch, an hour later, Bullett's bed was empty. I put down the plates I was carrying and raced out of the room.

"What's wrong?" Teddy called to me.

"Bullett!" I ran to the bathroom. The door was open. Duke was nowhere in sight. But Mr. Bullett was. He was submerged in the tub of water. I didn't have to pull his head out of the water to know he had already drowned.

I had been around the hospital long enough to realize there would be no inquest. What was a pathetic little pretzel like Mr. Bullett on the city hospital records? There was no family or friends to claim the body, or ask embarrassing questions. Death? Natural causes, obviously.

I reported the facts of the death to Kilpatrick. But

she, too, was by now immune to the kind of accident which, God knows, was familiar. "But aren't you going to do something about Duke?" I demanded. "Aren't you going to get him fired?"

"No," Kilpatrick said. "I'll give him a good cussing. But I won't get him fired. You don't know how scarce strong young male aides are, Louanne."

Duke didn't hate Bullett, I knew that. He just didn't give a damn. Like the woman who puts her baby on a table and then stands in the door chatting with a friend, while the baby rolls off and gets hurt. She didn't push him, she didn't even deliberately hurt him. Duke didn't shoot Bullett, but as far as I was concerned he had murdered him just the same.

I thought of going to the head supervisor myself. But I didn't. I knew what had happened, but my knowing wasn't going to bring that pathetic little old man back to life. It was one of my most difficult lessons in nursing to learn to hold my tongue.

In a hospital like ours, where patients die like flies, you can kill them with negligence, as Duke killed Bullett. You even can kill them with the best of intentions. The afternoon that Bullett drowned, we received an attractive, lively fifteen-year-old boy on our floor. A well-brought-up Negro boy, from a nice family, his aunt was an RN at another hospital nearby. This boy, Paul, had been pitching pennies with another kid right out in front of our hospital, on the sidewalk, when the two boys got into an argument about whose penny was lying closer to the line, and the younger kid pulled a knife and stabbed Paul in the

74

back with it. A passer-by brought Paul into the hospital and he was given emergency treatment, then sent to the ward. He was such a likable kid that we all paid a lot of attention to him, stopping by his bed to chat, and his aunt came to visit, and we all brought him gifts.

When any of us asked him how he felt, however, he said, "Oh, I have a pain." We thought he was just spoiled by all the attention, and nobody took him seriously, not even his aunt. "Oh, it's nothing, the wound just hurts him a little," she told me.

Three days later he died of infection. When he was brought into the hospital he had been given routine antibiotics, but apparently a deep-seated infection had developed anyway. And when he told us all that he "had a pain" he was telling the truth. It just happened that nobody believed him.

When there was no one else to help them, the patients often tried to help each other. Frequently they saved one another's lives. The ones who could get out of bed to go to the bathroom drifted from room to room, and kept informal watch on what was going on. If they found a patient in distress, they reported to the nurse. Some of the RNs hated these ambulatory watchdogs, but Kilpatrick didn't. She wanted to be where the emergency was. She was giving instructions to me one morning, after breakfast when one of the patients came for her.

"Quick, quick, the man in the oxygen tent needs you!"

We raced into the ward where he was pointing. A

coronary patient had been put in a canvas oxygen tent that morning. We looked at the bed—and all you could see was the opaque tent (today they are made of plastic and you can see the patient inside) with a hand clawing at the canvas. We ran over and checked the tank. The oxygen had run out and there was nothing inside that tent at the moment but suffocating heat. We got a fresh tank going in a few seconds, and the emergency was over. Theoretically the tents are supposed to be checked every fifteen minutes, but we didn't have enough personnel to do that.

Many times a patient would call one of us to report that a fellow patient had fallen out of bed. Besides the senile who often climbed out or fell out, we had a number of falls involving surgical patients. There was no Intensive Care unit connected with surgery at this time, and the patients were brought directly from the operating room to the ward where they received minimal care. Most of their falls occurred while they were still under the affects of anesthesia and were disoriented.

The one ambulatory patient we had who never showed any interest in his fellow patients was Jenner, the young Negro war veteran. A real loner, Jenner spent most of his time reading. He had no visitors, which surprised me since he was young and goodlooking and there surely must have been parents and girl friends in his life. He was a cardiac patient, and the resident seemed especially concerned about him. The orders came through to all of us on the staff that he did not want Jenner upset in any way.

I noticed that his lunch tray almost always came back untouched. I was considering reporting this to the resident, when Jenner himself appeared at the kitchen while I was preparing plates for lunch.

"Give me my tray in here," he said.

"I'm sorry, I can't," I told him. "I'm not allowed to serve patients in here."

"Then I won't eat," he said and walked back to the ward.

He didn't, either. I reported the incident to the resident. He went to talk to Jenner and then he dropped by the kitchen to see me.

"I think this is a case where we must relax the rules," the doctor told me. "He won't eat in the ward so I told him that you can feed him here."

I don't know what Jenner had against eating with the other men. He didn't seem psycho. He just wanted to eat by himself. He came to the kitchen for each meal and I fed him there. I was off duty one day and when I came back, Teddy told me that Jenner had refused to eat—even in the kitchen. It was like that the rest of his stay in the hospital. If I was on duty, he ate. If I was off duty, he ate nothing.

When he had first entered the hospital, an attendant had asked him for his money and jewelry so they could lock it up in the safe for him, but he had refused to give it to them. Then one day he came into the kitchen and handed me his army dogtag, a Bronze Star, and thirty dollars in cash.

"Keep it for me," he said. "I'll ask you for it when I'm ready to leave."

I didn't much like the idea of keeping his valuables for him and I asked Kilpatrick what to do with it. "A lot of patients don't trust the hospital," she told me. "If it makes him feel safer to leave his things with you, then keep them for him."

One morning when I got to work I found that Jenner had been discharged the night before. He had not asked me for his belongings and he did not have my address. I wondered what to do. I knew one thing I was not going to do, and that was to spend that thirty dollars!

Four months later Sis and I were on our way to a movie, when I saw Jenner on the street. I called to him and he recognized me and came over to us.

"I don't have your stuff with me now," I told him, "but let me give you my address and you can come pick it up."

"I don't want it," he said. "That was the only way I knew to thank you for being good to me." He glanced up the street. "Where are you chicks headed?"

"The movie—" I pointed to the theatre across the street. He walked over to the cashier's window with us, bought two tickets, handed them to us, said goodbye, and walked off.

"Who is that cat?" Sis asked me.

"I don't know,'" I told her. I don't think she believed me. But it was the truth. I never saw him again.

There were many patients in the hospital who really needed a nurse of their own. I guess the old ones got to me most. They seemed so sad and lonely and so neglected. And never more than they did at night. When I was put on a later shift for a few days when they were short of a night staff I discovered that many of our elderly patients cried all night long. This was when they felt most rejected, I suppose, by their families, by society, by those of us on whom they had to depend for whatever attention they could get. My little old friend Sol was one of the worst offenders. He was so sad he cried occasionally in the daytime. But at night he sobbed loudly all night long, and kept the other patients awake. I found that so long as I stayed beside him, and held his hand, he would be quiet. But the moment I left his side, he started up again. Since I couldn't be with him more than a few minutes and still get my work done, I began wondering what I could give him that might serve as a substitute—something that would reassure and pacify him so he could sleep. I thought of my little boys. After I had bathed them and tucked them in, if they seemed to feel lonely or frightened I had found that if I gave them something warm and sweet to drink it often helped put them to sleep. Many of the older patients who had trouble sleeping were bothered by phlegm in their throats which kept them restless and coughing. It occurred to me that a soothing syrup, such as I gave my babies, might relieve the old patients as well.

When I came on duty I sneaked in some baby bottles from home and made up a mixture of warm milk sweetened with Karo syrup. That night I tried out a bottle on Sol. He drank it all, and drifted off to sleep. The next day I brought more bottles, and gave them to the other elderly patients. Two of them bit the glass sippers, so the following day I brought rubber nipples and put them on the bottles. I had a hunch the doctors would have dressed me down if they'd caught me at it, but I found the old men were soothed by the whole baby routine: each night I'd clean them up, then tuck them in securely, as one does very young babies. Then I gave them their bottles of sweet warm milk to suck. They seemed to get the same sense of security out of this schedule that young babies do. I never did tell any of the other aides, and certainly not the nurses or doctors, what I did because I was sure no one would approve. But I had the quietest ward in the building, and it gave my younger patients a chance to get some much-needed sleep. Later I found out from aides who had worked in other city hospitals where they had a large census of elderly and senile patients that it is not unusual to treat them like babies. At these hospitals, when they were short-staffed on the night shift, it is routine to put diapers on the old patients.

Elderly patients expected to die in the hospital were referred to, by the staff, as "Old Crocks." Since the term was so commonly used by the doctors, nurses, and aides, and I was innocent of its real, and cruel, meaning (a broken-down, worn-out person), I assumed it was a medical term, like "cardiacs" or "trauma cases," and I picked it up—just as I had

80

picked up that catch-all hospital word "goof" for everything that went wrong, from being five minutes late to work to killing a patient accidentally.

I was feeding one of my elderly patients lunch a couple of weeks after I had begun giving bedside care, when a supervisor from the city's central nursing office appeared on our floor. It seemed that the daughter of one of the patients had gone to the city office and complained that her father had not been receiving his breakfast.

I had never seen this supervisor before but since I was doing my job I saw no cause for alarm. She approached the bed where I was working, and asked me if I had fed the patient about whom the complaint was made.

"No," I told her, and went on with my own patient.

"Why didn't you feed him?" she demanded.

"Because he's not my patient," I told her.

"What do you mean, he's not your patient?"

"I got these little old crocks in here," I explained, "and Jennie's got those old crocks over there where he is."

"*What* did you call those patients!" she demanded, blowing up like a pouter pigeon.

"Crocks," I repeated innocently, and went on with my feeding.

"Those are not crocks, young lady!" the supervisor corrected me sharply. "They are elderly men."

"Yes, they are too old crocks," I insisted. "That's what all the nurses and aides call them."

The city supervisor stared at me as if she couldn't

believe what she had heard, then flounced out in a huff. I went on feeding my patients. I still hadn't got the message that something had really gone wrong until I saw our own supervisor, Miss Adams, walk in.

"What did you do now?" she demanded.

She gestured impatiently at the spoon I was holding to my patient's mouth. "Hurry and finish."

"He can only eat so fast," I told her.

"Well, then, finish later. I want to see you. You are going to have to report to the nursing office at once."

"What did I do?" I asked, honestly puzzled.

"It was in reference to that patient not being fed," she whispered.

"You know he's not my patient."

"That's not it," she hissed. "You just saw our city supervisor and you goofed! Don't you know any better than to call the patients Old Crocks?"

"That's what you call them," I reminded her. "Where do you think I learned it from? I heard you say it. And I heard the other nurses and aides say it—"

"Ssh! Ferris, not so loud!" She peeked down the corridor to see if the city supervisor was still around. "It's just a sort of uh—slang—word we use now and then. But you're not to repeat it!"

I was feeling kind of bullish by now. I didn't like Adams anyway and I especially didn't like the idea of catching hell for imitating her. "If everybody else says it, why shouldn't I?" I asked stubbornly.

"Oh, you're hopeless." She marched off.

I went back to my ward. If I did have to report to the nursing office it could wait till I got through with my patients. I was still in there working, an hour later, when Adams came looking for me again. She gave me that phony little smile of hers and said that after careful consideration she had decided I did not have to report to the nursing office after all, and that she had personally called down and said it was not necessary for me to appear.

I learned later, from the other girls, that she had held a meeting with the other nurses and they had decided that since I had this bad habit of telling it like it is, they couldn't trust me to go to the nursing office. They knew damn well I'd tell the chief supervisor where I'd picked it up—and then they might all get in hot water. So Adams had phonied up some excuse to keep me off the hook.

But for the time being, she told me, I was under strict orders to stick to the kitchen and leave the patients alone till the whole thing blew over. She knew I was doing nursing duties, but if a doctor or head supervisor caught me at it, I might be picked up on charges, having already this other strike against me.

I didn't like that one bit. Slopping out food onto plates was my idea of nothing to do. One afternoon in June, about six weeks after I'd started to work at the hospital, my brother Jim gave me tickets to a championship fight. I didn't show up for work that night. The next day was a pretty warm summer day so I just decided to take a little vacation for myself and spend the time with the kids at the beach. I didn't report back to the hospital.

When Kilpatrick had let me start working with the patients and doing bedside care, I had had a taste of honey, and I didn't want to settle for anything less.

CHAPTER *FIVE*

The Making
of a Nurse

When I quit the hospital I had enough
cash to last a week or ten days, and
jobs were plentiful all over the city. Caring for patients
had meant more to me than any work I had ever done,
but being sent back to the kichen had made it mean-
ingless. I didn't want to continue washing and serving
dishes the rest of my life. I thought I'd have a little
holiday, then start job hunting again.

I had stayed away from the hospital about eight
days when I came home from the beach with my kids
one afternoon and found Lester waiting for me. I
had no telephone so he had come to personally deliver
a message.

"Miss Kilpatrick wants to see you. She's been covering for you, and writing in vacation days till you come
back."

Kilpatrick! I felt a twinge of guilt. I had gone off without talking to her. She was the one person to whom I should have felt responsible.

"Tell her I'll drop by tomorrow," I said.

Lester stayed long enough to have a cup of coffee and tell me he had missed me, and I found I was glad to see him again. He had a flirty, flattering way about him that made me feel good. It had been a long time since I'd had a man friend, and even when I had had Judson he was not one to give me compliments. If there was any praise floating around, he figured it belonged to him.

Next day, I got up, dressed, and checked into the hospital at seven A.M. I guess I'd known, subconsciously at least, that I would come back.

Kilpatrick called an aide to cover for her at the desk and she took me into the little nurse-doctor conference room, closed the door and gave me a cup of coffee.

"I want you back," she said bluntly. "Not just because you help me, but because of yourself. You have what it takes to be a nurse, Ferris. You enjoy patient care. You're good at it. You shouldn't leave now."

"But I'm not a nurse," I protested, "and I don't have a chance to be one. I can't go back and finish high school now."

"No, you can't," she agreed. "You're going to have to do it the hard way, step by step. But it is possible. Go down to the nursing office today and tell them you want to put in your application to be a nurse's aide. They let you train on the job, these days, when the hospital needs help so badly. I'll teach you everything you need to know."

"And what then?" I asked. "Nurse's aides get to be closer to the patient, it's true, but that's no big deal either. They only make four dollars a week more than I do, and there's no future in it."

"You can eventually train to be an LPN," Kilpatrick told me. She smiled. "No, Ferris, you won't ever get to be an RN. But just look what's happening to them. They get farther away from bedside patient care every day. And that's where you want to be. As a Practical Nurse, you will always be beside the patient."

My future was settled, wrapped up and delivered in that ten minutes. I've often wondered how my life would have gone if I hadn't crossed trails with that persuasive old she-devil, Kilpatrick.

Through her I had already acquired a number of the skills nurse's aides are taught. Procedures and experiences that had seemed frightening at first had already become exciting and challenging. Besides, Kilpatrick had already risked her professional standing by covering up for my missing days. It didn't occur to me to refuse—or even take time to consider—her proposal. "All right," I agreed. "I'm ready."

I went to the nursing office that morning and applied for a position as nurse's aide. Nurse's aides are supposed to go through a six-weeks training program, but in these early postwar years the hospitals were so shorthanded that the requirements had already been waived and I was allowed to train on the job under Kilpatrick and the other nurses. The first thing Kilpatrick showed me was the big nursing manual, which is kept on each floor.

"If you are in doubt, consult this," she told me. "It won't hurt you to study it when you have a free moment. And always remember, don't perform any medical procedure without consulting the nurse in charge. And whenever you see Dr. Durand coming on Grand Rounds, get out of his way. I don't want him to catch you doing nursing duties while you're still an aide."

"Dr. Durand," I repeated. "Which one is he?"

"Chief of Surgery," Kilpatrick told me. "You can't miss him—he's the biggest, roughest man around here—" She smiled—a smile of pure pleasure that was in contrast to what she'd just said. I wondered what she meant. I was soon to find out for myself.

A lot of nurse's aides are little more than personal handmaidens to the nurse supervisors. They spend all their time trotting out for coffee and Danish for the boss. Neither I—nor my self-styled teacher—had any intention of my becoming that kind of aide. Once my path was cleared through the nursing office, to become a nurse's aide, Kilpatrick started training me to do everything for a patient short of pronouncing death.

As well as having me make beds, take temperatures, and prepare bodies for the morgue, she taught me to take pulse rates and respiration—jobs that supposedly are done by RNs. If she was really jammed up at three-thirty, she asked me to work overtime. I often did. There was no overtime pay, but she made it up to me in her own fashion. When the weather was hot and the afternoon slow, she'd say, "Go on home early. I'll lend you a dollar. Take your kids to the beach."

She often sent me for supplies and medications so that she would not have to leave the floor in case of an emergency (which there was every few minutes), since she was the only one on the ward qualified to handle the life-saving equipment. The first time I turned up at the pharmacist's window I got the first full-fledged blast of discrimination that I had received since I went to work for the hospital.

According to the hospital rules, an employee could always go to the front of the line at the pharmacist's window, even though the medication he requested was for his own use. This was not generosity on the part of the administration, but because the employees were on paid city time and they wanted them to get back to their jobs as quickly as possible. But the pharmacist, who fancied himself on the level of the doctors, thought employees ought to go to the back of the line.

When I walked up front and presented my order the pharmacist glared through his cage at me, turned without a word, picked up a box and threw it in my face. I fielded it before it hit my nose, and stared at him. A thin, irritable, prissy-looking sort of man, with steel-rimmed spectacles and a permanent frown on his face, his eyes were filled with hate.

"So what have I ever done to you?" I asked him.

"Get on out of here and don't bother me," he snarled.

When I got back to the floor I asked Jennie about

him. "Oh, he's always like that—a real bastard," she told me. "Just wait till you have to ask him for medicine for yourself. He'll really make you sorry you got sick!"

"But what's he got against me?" I was still puzzled.

"You work here. And you're black." She smiled bitterly. "Just stay out of his way, Louanne. We've all tried—but there's no way of getting him fired. So we have to put up with him."

There was no discrimination on Kilpatrick's ward. Her idea, which transmitted to those of us who worked for and with her, was simply to try to get as much care as possible to our patients. They were lucky every day that she was personally in charge, as we all were to soon find out.

Kilpatrick's husband suddenly became gravely ill and she took off a few days to be with him. In her place we got a young Negro RN as floor nurse. She was on duty one morning when Big Joe, our asthma patient, suffered a severe attack. Kilpatrick, Jennie and I all had got to know Big Joe during the two weeks he had been on our ward and we were all fond of him. He never caused trouble; never made a fuss. He was a talkative man and since he was ambulatory we had all had our visits with him. Jennie and I were in the corridor, when Big Joe came out of the ward, wheezing painfully and clutching his chest. He walked up to the nurse's station and asked for adrenalin.

The new nurse got out his chart. "You've already had all that the doctor ordered," she said. "The order has expired. I can't let you have any more."

90

"Then call the doctor," Big Joe wheezed. "Tell him I need more." By now he was obviously in pain, and fighting for breath. His face was tense, the nostrils dilated.

The nurse put in a call for the doctor. "I'm sorry," she told Big Joe, "he's out for lunch."

"Page him," Joe pleaded.

She paged the doctors' dining room, but there was no answer.

"I'm sorry," she said to Joe. "I can't find him. Go back to bed. I'll try again later."

Slowly, Joe turned and walked back to the ward, clutching his chest and belly, both of which appeared taut and distended. His harsh, agonized breathing cut over the sounds of trays and wagons and food trucks in the corridor.

In a few minutes I heard him out in the corridor again. There was no mistaking that awful gasping.

Once again he leaned over the nurse's desk, clutching it so tightly that the white bone showed through his knuckles. "Please get me some adrenalin," he begged. "You've got to help me. I can't breathe."

My eyes automatically went to the nurse's pocket. I knew she had the keys to the drug closet. I also knew she was afraid to give the patient the medicine because nurses are never supposed to give medication except on doctors' orders. But he was in such distress, and adrenalin is not a narcotic.

"I can't," she told him.

Suddenly I wanted to run over and slap her, shake

her, take the keys away from her. I felt Jennie's hand on my arm.

"Why doesn't she do something?" I whispered angrily. "Why won't she give him the adrenalin? Can't she see how sick he is?"

"She's afraid," Jennie said. "Louanne, don't feel so hard about her. She's one Negro among fifty white nurses. It's worse if you are a Negro and break a rule. She's worked very hard to become an RN—"

"I don't care," I stormed. "I'd give it to him—even if it cost me my job!"

"Don't be too sure!" Jennie snapped.

I looked into Joe's face and felt chilled. He was already turning blue—cyanotic. I was in a rage of frustration. "Why doesn't he choke her?" I hissed. "Why doesn't he get those keys away from her?"

"Louanne, get hold of yourself!" Jennie said sharply.

But Big Joe was a meek man, not a raging animal like me. "Oh, please help me!" he begged in that gentle, gasping voice.

The nurse just shook her head and looked away.

Joe crept back to the ward. But he soon appeared again. By now he could no longer walk. He crawled to the desk, his hands in a praying position. "Oh, please help me," he whispered. "Please, please, Lord, help me. I'm dying . . ."

She just sat there. With the keys in her pocket. "I'm sorry," she said in a low, strangled voice. "I can't."

He crawled back to the ward. He could not lie down since he had to have his head elevated to get any air at

92

all. He clung to the bed, the empty adrenalin atomizer in one hand, then as he grew weaker, he slipped slowly to his knees.

"Please, please Lord, please . . ."

Mr. Smith got silently out of bed and placed his pillow between Big Joe and the wall. Old Tom handed his pillow to the surgical patient, who was now ambulatory, and he carried it to Joe.

I gathered up some extra pillows and we placed them around him, under his legs, and between his back and the wall. And then we all just stood there and watched him die. He lay gasping, at our feet, like a dog that's just been run over in the street.

Then he took that last, convulsive, choked breath and he was dead. I was raging inside and crying. But there was nothing I could do.

Jennie and I tied him up and took him down to the morgue, crying all the time we worked on him.

Next day, no one even mentioned it. One more Negro had died. One Negro RN had failed to get him medication. End of story. There was no investigation, not even any comment.

I often wondered how that nurse could live with her conscience. She might have lost her job if she had been discovered giving medicine without orders, it is true. But there were plenty of other jobs for trained nurses. She was married and had two small children. What kind of children would she raise, I wondered? What would she ever teach them about their obligation to their fellow man? What sort of values would they have?

I was still doing PMs along with my new duties, and one evening while I was working the midnight shift with Lester, a patient died. We had just begun to tie up that body when a second patient died. Then there was a third death. We had seven deaths in that one ward on a single shift.

"I wonder why?" Lester puzzled. "I've never seen them pile up quite like this."

I glanced out the window. "I know why," I told him. "Look there." I pointed to the night sky where the moon shone like a round, white plate. "You always get more deaths with a full moon."

He pooh-poohed my theory. But I knew I was right. When I worked in the emergency room later, we kept a record, and invariably we had the worst chaos on the nights when there was a full moon. There were the most automobile accidents, the most accidental deaths, the most stabbings and gunshots. Police who work in the ghetto precincts have found the same thing. They often put on extra force when there is going to be a full moon, because they know from past experience that the burglars, the psychos and the junkies will all go wild that night.

Lester and I were making rounds one night the following week, giving out water and checking on the sickest patients, when we came upon one patient who was lying quietly on his side, his hand on his cheek,

94

bed elevated, apparently asleep. He looked so peace-ful that we left him alone. The next morning when we turned on the lights to give the A.M. care and take the temperatures, this fellow was lying in exactly the same position. We checked him. He must have been dead for four or five hours.

When we find a body, the nurse writes a notation that the patient has "apparently ceased to breathe" and then sends for the doctor who pronounces death. Well, Lester and I agreed not to send for the RN or the doctor straight way on this one, because we were in trouble. Rigor mortis had already set in and the man's hand wouldn't come down off his cheek. We rubbed the arm and rubbed it and worked with it, and finally we got it so it would bend and lie flat against his side. Then we called for the RN and the doctor. Otherwise, we never could have prepared the body for the morgue.

Soon after that, Lester called in sick and I was alone on duty. Supper had been served and I thought I had everyone settled down, so I decided to study the nursing manual for a few moments before I gave out the medications. I was walking down the hall, when I noticed a giant of a Negro man—he must have been six foot four, 250 pounds and powerfully built, a real Joe Louis type—who had gotten out of his bed and was standing in one of the smaller wards. Lots of times the patients who are able to, do get out of their beds and go to the bathroom, or change the pillows or pull the bed farther out from the wall, so I didn't think anything of it. But when I came back past the ward twenty minutes later, I saw this fellow filling up the doorway. He was coming out of the ward door with his bed tied by the sheet to his back.

My God, I thought, I'm having nightmares. It can't be true. He had tied the bedsheet under the bedspring and then around his body so that he was dragging the whole thing behind him. I knew I had to do something fast. We had coronary patients in that room and if they became frightened it might be the end of them.

"Where are you going?" I asked him.

He glowered at me. "I'm going home."

"Is it necessary to take your bed with you?" I asked, trying to keep my voice gentle, and the fear out of it.

"Yes," he said. "Get out of my way."

"But you can't get on a bus to go home with that bed on your back." I tried to sound reasonable. As a matter of fact, I was scared blue.

He looked really wild; his face was all tense, his eyes glassy, his lower lip quivering. Perspiration was dripping off his face and arms. When he started toward me, I just backed up. This man was simply too huge and strong for me to tackle alone. I kept backing down the hall—toward the nurses' station, praying someone would appear who could help.

I glanced over my shoulder and saw a nurse sitting at the desk. She was a little bit of a half-pint Negro girl—no more than eighty pounds soaking wet. She looked up, saw us coming and stood up from the desk.

"What are you doing?" she demanded of the patient.

"Taking my bed home."

"You can't do that. Put it down," she ordered him. She stepped out from behind the desk, and started toward him. He ripped the sheet free, grabbed her chair from behind the desk and went for her.

I tackled him from behind, and just then a doctor appeared around the corner. "Doctor, over here!" I called to him.

The doctor looked up, so preoccupied that at first he didn't seem to realize what was happening in front of him. Then he saw the man with the chair in the air, and he rushed over and tried to wrestle it away from him.

I had hoped the doctor would think of a better way to approach the patient, but the fight was on. I raced to fetch help from another floor. Eventually, with the help of two male aides, the patient was subdued. By the time they led him back to bed the patient was limp as a used washcloth. All the fight was out of him. He was a very sick man.

The doctor put him in bed and gave him medication. The patient was just like a child the rest of the night. Next day they had a psychiatrist come over from the psycho building and check him. He said the patient was not mentally ill; that his behavior resulted from his physical illness, and that he need not be removed to the psycho ward. I guess the doctor knew what he was talking about because we had no more trouble with him. But that night I kept dreaming about him going after the little nurse with the chair. A couple of years later, one of our patients did go berserk and strangled a kitchen aide and then stuffed her body in a closet.

By morning I had a severe headache. I still had it when I went on duty hours afterward. The pain was at times so intense that I'd have to lie down for a moment before I could go on with my work. This went on for several days. I went to the clinic and the doctor on duty prescribed some pain-killing medication.

When I took the prescription to the pharmacist's window, he looked at it, tossed it back to me. "I don't have it," he snapped. "Next?" He craned past me to help the person in the front of the line. I didn't know what else to do except go back to my floor and try to work.

Within an hour I felt so bad I knew I had to have something. The pain was splitting my head.

I went back to the pharmacist.

He looked at me with obvious disgust. "What are you doing here? I told you I don't have that medicine."

"Isn't there something else you could give me?" I begged. "I'm in terrible pain."

"Later. When I'm not so busy."

I walked slowly back to my floor. My head felt as though there were a thousand knives sticking in it. I tried to work, but I couldn't, and I didn't have sense enough to give up and go home. Finally I went back down to the pharmacy for the third time.

"You've got to give me some kind of painkiller," I told him, "or I can't go on working. If you don't have what the doctor ordered, give me something else."

He glared at me, looked back at the shelf of medications, pulled out a box of pills and threw it through the window at me. "Here. Maybe that will keep you quiet."

As soon as I got back to my floor, I took two tablets. The doctors were getting ready to make rounds on that floor so the chief, the resident and interns were all standing in a knot near the nurses' station. I looked around at them as I dropped my paper cup of water in the trash can, and promptly fainted, at their feet.

It was the nicest feeling going down. I don't even remember hitting the floor. Since I collapsed in front of the group that had just assembled for rounds, I really had soup to nuts in the way of doctors, good, bad, and indifferent. They lugged me into a makeshift doctors' office and woke me up with their questions:

"Are you pregnant?"

"Do you smoke pot?"

"Do you drink wine?"

"Do you drink gin?"

"When did you last have intercourse?"

"Are you married?"

"How many children do you have?"

The questions were going around me like a great wheel turning. I tried to nod, to respond, but I could hardly hear them.

"Why don't you answer?" The doctor nearest me demanded in a loud voice.

"Because I can't hear you," I told him.

You should have seen the expressions on their faces.

My, they seemed to say, this is an interesting case! How nice.

Then they started all over again—loud and slow.

"When did you have your last period?"

I tried to answer as well and as truthfully as I could. But it felt as though I were on another planet—some great distance away from this circle of questioning faces.

"Do you drink?"

"Moderately. Three a day and I'm gone."

"Marijuana?"

"Never."

"Narcotics?"

"No."

"Pregnant?"

"Not to my knowledge."

Finally when I had answered their list, they let me tell them about my headaches. And after that, they sent me to bed in the female ward.

I had had the bottle of pills that the pharmacist gave me in my pocket. But I never saw it again. I was told later that when I passed out a nurse took the pills and threw them away to protect the pharmacist. I guess he was really angry with me, or just hated Negroes. Because what he had given me, I was told later, had temporarily hardened every muscle in my body and if I hadn't been a horse I never would have lived.

What I actually was suffering from was an infection of the middle ear which the clinic doctor had not detected, and I stayed in the hospital seven days. Now

the shoe was on the other foot: I was the patient—
at the mercy of whatever aide or nurse attended me.
I was supposed to get penicillin twice a day. I got
three shots in the entire week. When I told the doctor
who treated me that I was not getting the penicillin he
ordered, he told me to speak to the nurse. A lot of good
that did.

I was also supposed to be on a regular diet. And
I do have a good appetite. One day I was so hungry I
could have chewed up the sheet. The aide—a harassed,
unpleasant Irish girl whom I had never seen before—
brought me a tray with puréed meat on it like they
give to the toothless old patients. I asked for a piece of
meat. She said there wasn't any. I guessed the nurses
had stolen it all.

But I was hungry. And stubborn. I pointed to the
puréed meat, puréed peas and puréed potatoes. "That
is not my diet. I'm supposed to have a regular diet."

"Just who do you think you are?" the aide snapped
at me. "You'll eat what I give you."

"I'm an employee here, the same as you are," I told
her, "and I thought if I told you this isn't my diet,
you'd give me what I'm supposed to get."

"Listen," she growled, "if you don't want it, leave
it. Don't tell me you're an employee. You're nothing
but a bum!"

"I'm no bum," I shouted. "You call my supervisor.
I work here every day." Unfortunately, in those days
I hadn't yet learned how to swear and I didn't know
the words I needed. "I'm not going to eat this because it'll make me vomit."

"That's all you get." She went on to another bed.

I had seen a girl I did know in the hall with the food truck. So I climbed out of bed and went to the door to ask her for food.

I saw they did have some meat left over after all, and I was going to ask my friend to make up a sandwich for me. I was trying to attract her attention when the Irish aide noticed that I had left my bed and she came rushing over and barred the way into the corridor. She was furious with me.

"You get back in your bed and don't you dare come out here again."

"But I'm hungry," I insisted. "I just want to get some food to eat."

"I said leave."

"You've got your work to do. Just let me speak to my friend out here."

She gave me a push through the door back into the ward.

I don't believe in violence but when I looked up, there was my hand on her cheek. I didn't even remember raising it to strike her. It was just automatic reaction: she shoved me, I hit back.

The supervisor, who was being fed in the ward kitchen, heard the commotion and came out to see what was going on. She was a nice young nurse, no more than twenty-eight years old with rosy cheeks and glossy black hair and a good figure. Of course she was going to defend the dietary aide because that's where she got her meals, too. I turned and went back to bed and lay there crying, feeling sorry for myself. I was still hungry.

The supervisor walked over to my bed, the aide trailing her. "We are going to have to commit you to the psycho ward for striking an employee."

That made me sit up and stop crying. "You will, will you? Then you better commit both of us," I said, "because she pushed me."

Just then the chief supervisor strode in. I never had known her to get in on a little fracas like this before. I guess they all thought it was really serious. She marched over to my bed just like a drill sergeant.

"What's going on here?" she demanded in a big, booming voice.

Before I could say anything, the pretty supervisor told her boss what had happened. When I listened to what she said I was glad she was doing the talking. Because she was a fair girl and she told it like it really was. Then she ended up saying she was sending me to the psycho ward for striking another employee.

"You're going to do what?" boomed the chief. She pointed to the Irish aide. "You pushed her. She hit you. That's the end of it. Give her some food." She turned around and marched out.

In a few minutes the Irish aide appeared with a sandwich and shoved it at me. I was afraid to eat it. Hungry as I was I was sure there must be a little strychnine tucked in with the mayonnaise.

CHAPTER SIX

The Saddest Ward

When I became a nurse's aide my salary went up sixteen dollars a month (I now got seventy dollars each two weeks) and I never had to work in a kitchen again.

After training on the male ward with Kilpatrick, my first assignment as nurse's aide was to care for the patients in the Tubercular Solarium. This is a small ward located in the main building of the hospital which serves as a sort of way station for TB suspects. They are held there from three to six weeks while tests and X-rays are made. If their tests come out positive they are transferred to the Tubercular Ward, which is a separate building on the hospital grounds. If their tests are negative they are released and sent home— provided, meanwhile, they don't contract the disease from the infectious positive patients.

The Solarium is supposed to be partially isolated. About the only isolation it actually has is from good medical care, since it is always so crowded that the patients spill out into an alcove in the open corridor. These particular patients, more than any others in the hospital, exist in a sort of limbo between dismissal and care. Since they are not clearly either resident or transient, they belong nowhere in the hospital system. And they don't seem to be anyone's particular responsibility.

Besides, most of the people who work in the hospital are afraid of the patients in the Solarium and they will do anything to avoid touching them. No one wants to go into that room. It seems ironic, when you stop and think that a few years ago most of us, including a lot of doctors, assumed that tuberculosis was a disease of the past; that it was under control and no one would die of it anymore. Yet ten thousand people do die of TB each year in the United States—and most of them are poor, and non-white, because today tuberculosis is a disease of poverty. It results from the way poor people live: bad diet, exposure, exhaustion, absence of preventive care, etc.

I saw it happen in my own family. My sister-in-law, a beautiful girl with straight long black hair and bronze skin who looked like my idea of Pocahontas, and was my husband's favorite sister, married in the South, then moved North. She had several children, her husband failed to support her, and she was too proud to tell her family what was happening and to ask their help until it was just too late. By the time she dragged herself and her kids back home to Alabama, she was already dying of tuberculosis, which had been brought on by malnutrition and exposure. It nearly killed my husband to come back from service and find his lovely sister in that condition. That was why he was staying in the South. He felt the least he could do for her was to be with her until she died.

Most of the hospital workers are poor people, too, and they have good reason to fear the tuberculars. TB is still our most deadly communicable disease. Each year, we had an average of seven new cases of TB among the hospital workers.

I felt in part this must be due to carelessness, because we are taught how to protect ourselves. I wasn't frightened or nervous at the thought of working with the tuberculars until I walked into the Solarium that first morning.

I thought I had seen neglected patients on the male ward. But they couldn't compare with the conditions that greeted me here. There were eighteen beds jammed up close together, none of them made. Instead of changing the beds, the aides had simply pulled up the sheets (which they could do without actually touching the patients) to make it look as though the patients had received care, and the linen had not been changed for days. It was a dirty gray and soaked with sputum, some of it blood-streaked, from the patients' coughing, and hemorrhaging.

The urinals were full and lying around on the nightstands and the floor. The bedpans had not been emptied for days and they were lying on the floor and on the chairs reserved for visitors, with week-old newspapers covering them. There were balls of dust under the beds and on top of the nightstands. Dried fruit pits littered the floor.

I was standing there, just wondering where to begin, when the patient nearest me plucked at the sterile gown I had put on over my uniform.

"We haven't had any breakfast today. This is the third day we haven't had any breakfast. Will you give us some?"

Amid the other debris that cluttered the tables, I had noticed medical test trays, with the bottles, jars, and equipment which is used for taking blood specimens, for Wassermann and chemistry tests. Those trays, too, were covered with dust.

"How long have those test tubes and bottles been there?" I asked the patient.

"Since Sunday night," he told me.

That explained why the patients had received no breakfast. Breakfast is always held back on the morning that the blood work is due to be done by the doctors. The test trays had been brought in on Sunday night so that the doctors could take the samples early Monday morning. This was Wednesday and the samples had not yet been taken. For three days the patients had been deprived of their breakfasts while the trays sat there gathering dust.

That made me furious. It was one thing for an

ignorant aide to be afraid of a patient—but for the doctors to be afraid! I was still too young to know enough to keep my mouth shut. I snatched up one of the trays and marched out to the nurse's desk and held it under her nose.

"Just look at this!" I said. "I think it's a damn shame that the doctors are so afraid of those patients in there that they won't come and draw blood. If they're too chicken to do it, the least they could do is tell us so that we could get those people some food. This is eleven A.M. on Wednesday. They didn't get their breakfast this morning. They didn't get any yesterday morning. Or the morning before that. And all because the doctors are afraid to touch them!"

The nurse murmured something sympathetic and said she'd see what she could do—all the while giving me the high sign to shut my big mouth and get a load of who was listening. I turned around and found the resident doctor in the corridor behind me. I had boiled out of that room so fast I hadn't noticed him standing there.

If looks could kill, he would have got me. But he said nothing. Few doctors have any truck with anybody as lowly as a nurse's aide. But I was so mad I didn't care if he had heard me. Every word I had said was God's truth. I just turned and walked into the supply room and got my tray set up with alcohol and soap and water and towels and went back to my ward to start cleaning up those hungry, dirty patients of mine.

108

As soon as I was out of earshot, of course, the resident made his comments to the nurse about my fresh behavior. He also found the chief supervisor and told her. She got him calmed down and out of the way and then she came into the ward to see me. She did not penalize me, as I'm sure the doctor expected her to do. But she did give me a warning.

"You're a good worker and I'm not going to call you up for this," she told me, "but there is something you better learn right now, Ferris, or you will never last in the hospital." She shook her finger under my nose for emphasis. "*A nurse cannot dictate to a doctor.* And that's not just you aides, that means a PN, or an RN, too. I don't care how right you are. You must watch what you say. That doctor could call you up on charges and get you fired with no trouble at all. Don't you forget that. And there's another thing I want you to think about, Ferris," her voice was softer now and I knew she was reaching for my understanding. "That man is more needed in this place than you are. He's a doctor and what he does for these patients is more important than what you do for them. Understand?" She gave my arm a sharp pinch, and started out of the ward. "I'll see that you are cleared to proceed with the morning care."

As I worked I realized that what the supervisor said was true. I could think I was the best aide in the world, but they could still hire, train, or fire a dozen of me. They had to have doctors. And already I had heard that the hospital was finding it harder than ever to find men who would work in a city hospital. Within a few years we would get most of our doctors from other countries.

When the permission came through to go ahead with the patient care I asked for assistance since most of these patients were not supposed to get out of bed, and some of them needed to be turned, which was a two-man job. A male aide, who was not afraid of the tuberculars, was sent in to help me, and together we went about the monumental job of getting all the patients cleaned up, their beds changed, and eventually getting them fed.

When we went to turn one emaciated, elderly man we found that he had both urinated and evacuated in his bed and for some reason I shall never know, there were eight one-dollar bills stuck in the wet feces.

We were still working with him, when an ambulatory patient ran out of the patients' bathroom and said, "Come quick, there's a man in here, hemorrhaging."

We both rushed in. The patient—a young, thin Puerto Rican—was sitting on the toilet, his head lying in the washbasin, coughing his lungs out. Each time he coughed, the blood gushed forth in a sheet of bright red froth that sprayed over the sink and the wall above. We picked him up and carried him in our arms back to his bed. He never stopped coughing and by the time we reached the bed, both of our gowns were soaked with blood. We rushed to the supply room and got sandbags to pack around him and immobilize his body. Then I snatched up a sheet and we dumped into it all the ice we had in the ward, to fashion a makeshift icepack, and we packed that around him. We were both too busy trying to stop the hemorrhage to leave to call the doctor. We were still working over our patient at fever speed when he suddenly spewed forth a last curtain of blood, then fell back dead. It was the quickest, bloodiest death I had ever seen. Both of us were as drenched as though we had spent the day butchering pigs.

I worked in the Solarium for six weeks. My outburst may have momentarily endangered my job, but it had served a purpose. After that, the blood samples were drawn on schedule and the patients did not miss any more breakfasts. I heard, through the hospital staff grapevine, that the resident had called in the interns who were responsible for drawing the blood, and chewed them out for their negligence.

When the Solarium patients' tests came back positive, they were transferred over to the tubercular building. The tubercular building at our hospital is a world unto itself, like nothing else. It is a regular little battleground, the hotbed for crime and violence in the hospital. Many of the patients have knives, guns, narcotics, and booze. If a patient hasn't got more than twenty-nine cents to spend he can still buy a little bottle of Twister or Rose Heart wine from one of the hospital employees or from another patient. There's a regular traffic in liquor there, as well as a thriving business in narcotics and numbers. There must be drinking going on every night in that building, because when I come to work in the morning I can always count eight or ten empty wine bottles in the courtyard of the building, and the courtyard is swept each night.

There is also always plenty of evidence of narcotics. The patients, visitors and staff are not checked as they come in, and even if they were, the narcotics users have all sorts of cute tricks—like tying ropes on packages and pulling them up the outside of the building and in through the window. Also, the syringes which we use in the hospital are not broken and destroyed, as they should be, but simply thrown out with the general garbage. Recently a tubercular patient was found selling used hospital syringes as well as narcotics to other patients.

You will always find a prosperous bar near every city hospital, as well as a package store and a check-cashing establishment. The owner of our particular bar has made enough money off the hospital to add a restaurant and to put his kid brother through college. A number of hospital employees keep beer and liquor accounts at the bar so that they can always buy for themselves, the other employees, or for the patients. Not long ago, a nurse in the TB building caught a porter coming on the ward with a big gift-wrapped package which he claimed was a birthday present for his wife. She asked him to open it. The box contained forty-eight pints of Twister wine. The porter still claimed it was intended for his wife, to use to make a punch for her birthday party. The nurse confiscated the box, but returned it to the porter when he went off duty. The day after that I counted twenty instead of eight empty Twister bottles in the courtyard, so he must have smuggled the box back into the ward. And he apparently saved a little for himself because he came up missing that afternoon and when they finally found him he was propped up in the linen closet, thoroughly ossified. He was so stiff it took the supervisor, the nurse and two aides to drag him out.

Many of the tuberculars are ambulatory. They bribe the employees to smuggle street clothes in to them, so that they can dress and go over to the bar or luncheonette for a drink or a sandwich and then sneak back into the hospital in time for bed check.

I can sympathize with their wanting to get out once in a while, but I don't like the idea of their spreading TB germs in those public places. We all go to the luncheonette—aides, nurses, doctors and their wives and kids. I've often wondered what a doctor feels like when his own wife or child turns up a positive tubercular. It makes the waitresses angry, but I refuse to drink out of a chipped or rough-edged cup, because I know it can't be sterile. The only way you can get the germs off a cup like that is to scrub it with a brush and soap, and you know the coffee shop doesn't do that.

The real tragedy of the TB building is that most of the tuberculars are young people, and when they go there only a small percent have hopes of getting out.

It's a resident population that lives at the hospital, months, years. Most of them have no other home. More than once we've had a woman patient enter the tubercular building, become pregnant, be transferred to the maternity section until the baby is born, then return to the tubercular ward. Some men and women meet, become engaged, and marry in the tubercular building.

There's more sex going on in the TB ward than anywhere else in the hospital simply because you have so many young people living there with nothing else to do. A nurse's aide, who is a friend of mine, was making supply rounds one evening, when she walked down a poorly lighted stairway between floors in the tubercular building and stumbled across a pair of patients engaged in sexual intercourse. When she scolded them, instead of breaking apart, the couple remained entwined and the man told the aide to shut up and go away.

"Mind your own damn business," he hissed at her, "and at least let me finish!"

The aide didn't know what to do then. Since it was obvious she wasn't going to persuade them to break it up and go back to their beds, she left them where they were and ran to tell me about it.

"You should have just walked over them," I told her, "and if you didn't like what they were doing, you could write up a report. That's all you can do anyway. Besides, he wasn't killing her. That was just human nature taking its course. What right did you have to stop them?"

114

There is a big, handsome Negro nurse who has been working in the TB building since it opened. She's a real bull shit artist and a great favorite with the doctors. Married, with two kids, she was probably about thirty-five or thirty-six years old at the time we received a very handsome male Negro patient in the Solarium whose tests came out positive and who was sent over to the TB building. He wasn't feeling too sick and he soon got in the habit of hanging around the desk, talking to this nurse. Around eleven each morning everyone in the hospital who can get away with it takes a coffee break, or sneaks a snooze on a stretcher somewhere, or reads or knits for a few minutes, and the word went around that this nurse disappeared at this time every morning and no one knew where she was. Then, one of the ambulatory patients happened to want to use the toilet at 11:15 one morning, and he walked into the male patients' bathroom and lo and behold, there was our nurse enjoying sex on the floor with her pet patient.

Well, she had the presence of mind to scream, "Rape!" which shows you she never stopped thinking. And she was such a good nurse and such a favorite with the medical staff that they kept her—and threw out the patient.

The patient, however, was not a stupid man, and he went before the Board of Health and told them that the nurse was a liar; that they had been having sexual relations ever since he had been in the ward. He was eventually admitted to another hospital. But

I always did feel that our hospital got rid of the wrong person.

Like most city hospitals, ours is eaten up with the numbers game. The worst thing about numbers is who's at the top—namely, the Mafia. Other than that I can't get too excited about numbers as crime because for so many people who live in the ghettos, the numbers buy hope. It's often the only hope they have. A welfare mother can save out a nickel and put it on a number and hope for $25—which may mean new shoes all around for her kids. A dime hopes for $50, which is still a fortune in the ghetto. A quarter might get you $125. A dollar can win $500. . . . It's a real long shot, but when somebody does win, everybody in the neighborhood rejoices, and then they all have a little hope to live on, to sweeten the bad days. Police in ghetto areas often don't bother to make more than an occasional token arrest for numbers. They know, poverty being what it is, they will never put the numbers down, so they save their energies for violent crime. Violence crops up in the numbers racket, too, when a collector tries to hold out on the bosses upstairs. And of course everybody who places a bet supports the big crime syndicate. But violence seldom touches the bettors.

You place your bet by guessing what the last three digits of the day's take (the Total Mutual Handle) at the races will be. Nearly every large building in every large city has its own resident collectors. In ghetto areas the collectors work by the block and are usually well known to everyone who lives there. They work a block of houses or an apartment or office building, taking up the bets for the day, "writing the numbers" for each bettor, and then they turn these slips of paper over to the syndicate's controller. The controller in turn delivers the bets to pickup stations or directly to the syndicate's bank. There other syndicate employees sort and record the bets and when the winning number for the day is announced at the track, the bank notes the winners. Winners get paid either that same night or the next morning by their collectors.

It is a poor people's game, but it is not confined to any one race. Negroes are heavy bettors, but so also are Italians and Jews and every other race that lives in slum or lower middle-class areas, who need to buy a dream. White housewives in lower middle-income housing developments are some of the biggest numbers bettors.

The control at the top of the syndicate is Italian and Jewish. These are the big shots, the bosses, that the individual bettor never sees. Often the bank employees and controllers are also Italian or Jewish. The lowest level of the racket, the local collectors, are apt to be Negroes and Puerto Ricans. In the hospitals it often is the male employees who also work as collectors for the other employees and the patients, although some women are in the game too. One handsome, grayhaired, grandmotherly looking nurse's aide who used to dress at the locker next to mine got picked up selling numbers to the patients lined up in the Emergency room. She was convicted, and had to serve a year's sentence, besides losing her job. She was a good nurse, and had a family of which she was very proud and it seemed a pity to me, for her to ruin her life like that when she could have got along on her salary without getting involved in a racket.

I learned about the numbers game before I ever came North. While I was still living in Alabama, after Judson had gone in the army, I had, for a neighbor a woman I should have had sense enough to be scared of, except I was young and lonely and she gave me things for the baby, and I liked her. She was a skinny, old Creole woman, by the name of Miss Mag. I recognized that she was witchy—but I didn't know until later, when I got it all pieced together, that Miss Mag had every vice in the world going for her.

It's really wonderful to be dumb. When you get smart there's not much fun left in things—just like when you learn there's no Santa Claus, Christmas doesn't mean much any more. I was already married and had a baby when I met Miss Mag, but there was a world of things I just didn't know.

The first thing she taught me was a dirty word. She had a husband—a quiet shadow of a man who sort of hung around the house and got his meals there, but he didn't seem to be any more part of the activity than that—and she called him the "old cock-knocker." In fact, it was the only name I ever did hear her call him. She used it behind his back and to his face and she always said it in such a nice, soft voice that I

118

thought it was just some kind of affectionate nickname, and I picked it up. I was talking to a young man, a friend of my husband's, one day, and he said something funny and I laughed and said, "Why, you cute old cock-knocker!"

He looked surprised, but he didn't say anything. However, another friend of mine, an older woman, had heard me say it and she couldn't wait till he was out of earshot to pounce on me. "Do you know what you said?"

Then, before I could even admit that I didn't, she let me have it, and told me exactly what the words meant. Well, I was so embarrassed I never was able to look that young man in the eye again.

The next trouble Miss Mag got me into was the numbers racket. She knew I needed money and wasn't able to work because of the baby.

"How would you like to do a little job for me and pick up some money without having to go out to work to do it?" she asked one day.

"Oh, I'd like that." I was all eagerness without a thought in my birdbrain head except money.

"Well, I've got an easy little job for you, honey," Miss Mag told me. "All you have to do is just go around to the houses in the block while you're out wheeling your baby each morning, and put down the number each person gives you in this little book, and then bring it back to me."

So I started writing numbers for the block. I'd been doing it for several weeks, and dutifully collecting for Miss Mag, who paid me off a couple of dollars each day, when I heard that an arrest was going to be made in our neighborhood.

"The cops are ging to make a pinch"— one of the women in the block told me; I must have looked blank, because she went on—"an arrest, stupid. They're going to take in a man."

"Who did he kill?" I asked.

"Nobody. You don't have to kill somebody to get arrested! He's been writing numbers."

Then I realized what that little black book I had tucked in the baby's blankets meant! I was really shook up. Not only frightened, but it rocked me to realize I had been committing a crime. I couldn't wait till I got back to Miss Mag's house and turned her little black book back to her—once and for all.

Miss Mag never was arrested. She sold numbers for over twenty years to my knowledge without ever getting caught. But then, she was a very clever woman. She was always calling the local cop to come in and have a chicken leg or a slice of watermelon.

It didn't take me long to discover that whenever you find a hospital employee living higher than his wages would allow—like owning a house of his own or a big car or being able to send his kids to college—you can pretty well be sure he is selling digits. We've had a half-dozen employees picked up for writing numbers since I've been at the hospital, and then we have a couple of others who, like Miss Mag, are smart enough to keep right on doing it without getting caught.

One of our well-known collectors is a big, rangy, comical character, named Diller. Besides numbers, he likes to booze it up, and since I've been in the hospital he has been demoted from practical nurse to nurse's aide, to kitchen aide, to porter. They never have got enough on him to fire him, but he's always in some kind of hot water. He worked in Obstetrics for a while, until some of the younger women patients complained that he was always peeking over the screen at them when they were in the examination room. Then they transferred him to X-ray and he got a few feels there, too, helping ladies on and off the table, but I guess the patients were in too much pain to notice, because he was demoted from that position for snoring off a hangover in the developing room. But, when it came to numbers, Diller really played it cool. Twice he has been picked up, but both times the cops had to let him go. They cannot convict anyone of being a number collector unless they can find a certain number of digits on his person. And they never were able to catch Diller with the numbers—although everyone knew he was one of the busiest collectors at the hospital. Lester told me that the reason Diller never got caught was because he had a sure-fire method of keeping out of jail: every time he saw a cop heading his way (and he had his own spy system in the hospital so that he got advance warning when the police did appear) he simply chewed up and swallowed whatever numbers he happened to have on his person at the moment.

One of the resident patients in the TB building is

said to have amassed a fortune of nearly two million dollars on numbers and loans in the years he has lived here. But I doubt that story. Because I believe the only people in numbers with that kind of money are the bosses. Just as it is true in the narcotics racket. The little pushers that the individual addict buys from are not the racketeers who can afford to give their daughters the fancy ten-thousand-dollar weddings.

The real numbers king in our hospital was Lester's friend the night guard, Ollie, who kept his "office" down in the subbasement furnace room. I had yet to meet Ollie face-to-face, but I had heard all about him. ("You want a number today, Louanne? Go find Ollie.") I don't know what kind of money Ollie pulled down as a collector, but it must have been a sizable amount, because he was so important to the syndicate that his controller came to him to pick up the collection of numbers each day. Lester pointed the controller out to me not long after I started to work at the hospital. He was a young, slender, good-looking Italian who simply drifted in and out of the hospital as he chose. No one stopped him.

Security was a farce, those days, at the hospital. We had a handful of elderly guards, retired from other jobs, who couldn't begin to keep up with the civilian traffic that flowed in and out of the hospital complex. It seemed like anybody could just walk into the hospital anytime. You never knew who people were. Patients, visitors, staff, hoods, lovers, dope pushers, imposters. We had everything going through those corridors, and most of us were so busy getting our own work done we didn't pay much attention.

One day a neatly dressed white man, with a stethoscope hanging around his neck, turned up at the Female Ward and announced he was Dr. Soandso come to see his patients. There was a flirty young nurse on duty, and he was a good-looking man, so she giggled and hiked her skirt and welcomed him in, although she had never seen him before—those young ones don't ask questions when they think they've found somebody to play games with.

About thirty minutes later, a surgeon came in to check a patient, saw the stranger in the ward, and said, "Who the hell is examining my patient?"

The nurse jumped up, all flustered. "Why that's Dr.—"

"Doctor who?"

She either remembered the name he gave or made up one. "Dr. Barnes."

"There is no Dr. Barnes in this hospital. Call for a security officer."

By this time the hokey doctor had heard the exchange, and hotfooted it out the back door. The surgeon gave chase, but the other man had a good lead. He must have slipped out a window and onto the fire escape because they never did find him.

When they checked to see what mischief he'd been up to they found he had been giving vaginal examinations, and had got his hand into three ladies before he'd been flushed.

Another flagrant violation of security occurred that spring when we received a king of the gypsies for a patient. When I got off the bus in front of the hospital the morning after he was admitted, I could hardly believe what I saw. It was as if someone had played a practical joke during the night and converted the hospital grounds into a stage set. There must have been forty gypsy families camped out on all the available green space inside the iron fences in front of the hospital buildings.

When I walked into Receiving, I did another double take. It was like walking inside a gypsy tent. The gypsies had taken over both the main room and the little anteroom. Other visitors had given up and stood in the halls, or had gone home.

The few benches had been converted into beds for the gypsy children, with blanket rolls stretched out on them. The tables were littered with pretty china cups and plates. Hot plates were plugged in the wall outlets. Copper teakettles sang merrily. Plump, older gypsy women, looking even plumper in their many skirts, moved purposefully around the room, tending their household chores. One of them had even found a broom in the porter's closet and was calmly sweeping the floor.

They had moved in. We were the outsiders. I looked over to the aide at the Receiving desk. She shrugged, spread her hands helplessly. We were the ones who were upset and confused, not the gypsies.

Late that morning the administration marshaled our

elderly little band of security officers and they came and swept the gypsies out of Receiving. They retreated as far as the camp in the front of the building, and as soon as the security men had scattered, came in again. It was like ants or locusts—you put them out the back door and they come in the front.

When the word went to the administrator that the gypsies were again in possession of the Receiving room, he didn't bother to order them put out. Instead, he concentrated on an arrangement to have the gypsy king transferred to a nursing home as soon as possible.

But while the king was still with us, the gypsy women plied their trade with the patients and the employees at the hospital. They seemed to be everywhere, in the corridors, waiting rooms, they even turned up in patient treatment rooms—wagging their playing cards and dream books, trying to pick up a sucker for a fortunetelling. One cunning lady smuggled in her crystal ball and was discovered divining the futures of the poor patients lined up awaiting treatment on the benches in the emergency room.

After the gypsy invasion, we got a few more guards added to our security force, but it didn't seem to affect the presence of the Mafia. The syndicate men were easy to recognize, with their dark glasses and pretty silk suits, and their Cadillac cars. Ollie's controller was the only one who regularly came into the hospital. The others circulated outside the hospital on paydays. You'd see them parked along the street outside, waiting to pick up one of the employees. Not for numbers, but for loans. The syndicate also controls the loan shark operations in the ghettos, and Negroes and Puerto Ricans are their principal customers—victims might be a better word. Many of these poor people are not smart about money. They always want something they don't have, and sharpies con them into borrowing the money they need to buy it: it may be a television set, or a wedding ring or a new car. Then they extract exhorbitant interest rates from the poor suckers who accepted their money. And if the suckers don't pay, the syndicate men start in threatening them. Next comes roughing them up to scare the bejeesus out of them, so that they will get the money any way they can—from friends, family, or maybe they're so scared they steal it to pay off the boys in the silk suits. If they don't pay, they are beaten—as a warning to the others. Some are killed.

The syndicate also uses some city hospital out patient clinics as a distribution center for narcotics. They don't swipe the hospital's drug supply. They bring in their own, then have someone on the staff distribute the drugs to their buyers, at the same time that the hospital drugs are being distributed to the patients. In that crowd of patients, and with the lax security, the syndicate buyer and seller can meet and transact their business without attracting anyone's attention.

Once when I was temporarily on the information desk in the reception room, to replace someone who had called in sick, I spotted a man who must have been a detective coming in every day and sitting around. I guess he was looking to pick up someone in the narcotics traffic. But he was wasting his time. He had put on old clothes and was wearing dirty old sneakers, but he had cut a hole in the side of his sneakers and you could see that he had on clean white socks. Also he'd forgotten to take off his handsome wrist watch. With those clean socks and that wrist watch, who did he think he was fooling? Certainly not any man smart enough to survive in numbers or drugs.

I was escorting a positive TB suspect from the Solarium over to the TB building one morning, when I ran into the deputy superintendent of the hospital coming out of the TB building. I guess he was so upset he had to show somebody—or maybe he just felt called upon to explain the peculiar collection of stuff he was carrying. He had a couple of empty liquor bottles, several homemade daggers and a collection of numbers slips. "Look at this!" he growled helplessly to me. "Just look at what I picked up in there this morning!" He shook his head in despair. "Numbers, whiskey, fights—you name it. We've got it!"

He went on down the stairs, muttering to himself.

I stayed with my patient until we had checked him in and found him a bed. While I was there three ambulatory TB patients appeared back on the ward from the emergency room, with fresh bandages on their heads. "What happened?" I asked Eva, a prim, quiet little aide who worked in TB.

"You just should have been here!" She rolled her eyes to heaven. "If you ever want entertainment, you just walk over here! We got our little parties going every night. And when they get dull, they start getting out the daggers and the knives. Look at that"—she pointed to one of the patients who had a wide bandage across his forehead, another on his arm—"forty-seven stitches, Louanne! With a homemade dagger!"

From what I pieced together from Eva and the other aides who work there, it goes on every night: drinking bouts, knife fights, the works. And there is simply not enough staff or security to control it. Many of these patients are young and fairly strong despite their illness. And they have nothing to do with their time—except booze it up, fight it out, or try for sex.

I feel that if the hospital provided some kind of full schedule programs of recreation and rehabilitation for those people, they wouldn't get into so much trouble. Many of them will be released from the hospital sooner or later. If their life there has been little more than a round of drinking and fighting, they will do the same thing on the city streets. Many of them will end up in jail. Yet, they are not necessarily criminals. If their hospital time could be spent constructively, learning something they could use for better employment when they get out, the city would benefit in the long run.

There is a so-called Recreation Program for the tubercular patients, but it's a farce. The Recreation leaders do what they can with the funds they have to work with, but it doesn't amount to much more than old movies once or twice a week, and a little cookout with wienies and punch three or four times a year. That's hardly enough to fill up the hours for young, vigorous, ambulatory patients.

The real roadblock to anything being done for the patients is the Chief of Rehabilitation. A white doctor, he pulls down a sizable salary, but there's no question about his bias against Negroes and Puerto Ricans. At a staff meeting in the presence of a number of black doctors and nurses he announced that if any son of his ever married a black girl he'd be cut off from the family. A friend of mine, Mary, a trained teacher who was once dean of students at a college, works under him. Mary has a marvelous way with young people—the kind of cheerful, inspiring disposition that really gets through to them. But her boss sees to it that her hands are tied. After she had had very good luck rehabilitating one teenager who was released and able to get and hold a good job because of her work with him, she went to her boss and told him about the case. "Now that's just one boy," she said, "and he was all I could care for at one time. But if there were several more of us, each working with one of the patients who will be released, it could make a lot of difference."

"We don't have that kind of a budget," the doctor told her.

She was all fired up with her little success, however, and she tried to argue with him. "But isn't it more important to the city to care for people so that they can lead a decent life when they leave here—than to have them as criminals on their hands?"

"We don't have funds for any more employees," he told her flatly. "I'm sorry."

"What about working out some kind of educational

program with volunteer instructors?" she pressed on.

"I'm not interested in that kind of program," he told her.

She was getting mad by then. "I don't think you're interested in Negroes or Puerto Ricans," she snapped, "as long as you get your salary!"

He had her called up on charges for that. But for some reason she didn't get fired. Maybe the hospital could get few other trained employees to work for the salary she drew.

CHAPTER SEVEN

The Winter's Toll

The more I handled patients, the more I realized that all of them, male and female, black and white, are frightened. Weakened by illness, accident or whatever brought them to the hospital, their defenses are very low. Every sour expression, harsh word, or whispered confidence among doctors and nurses throws them into a private panic, and confirms their most dire fears about their own condition. It never ceased to amaze me the way doctors could stand over a patient and discuss his case in precisely the same way that repairmen might consider the possible treatment of a burned-out refrigerator motor. The fact that the ill or maimed body they were favoring with their technical concern might also have a heart and a brain simply didn't seem to occur to them. I guess they figured the patients ought to be grateful to get any attention.

I was assigned to the women's ward one morning to

prepare an elderly lady for surgery. I had been trained to approach the patient quietly and explain in a soft voice whatever the medical procedure was, before I began it. Unfortunately, my patient was hard of hearing. I had brought in my little cart of supplies, told her what I was going to do, but she only stared at me uncomprehendingly. I raised my voice a little and was suddenly aware that it was the only sound in the entire ward—which was odd, since the ward was usually quite noisy.

I looked around. A group of doctors had just come into the room, obviously on Grand Rounds. But there was something special about this particular Grand Rounds—and I took a second look to see what it was. Instead of the young doctors wandering in scattered formation, the chief somewhere in their midst, these young doctors were all grouped into a tight, frightened little covey, clearly to the side and behind their leader. He towered in the doorway—a huge, ruggedly handsome man in his early forties—at least two inches over six feet, and a good 220 well-packed pounds, with high coloring: brilliant blue eyes, reddish blond curly hair and florid skin. I realized this must be the doctor Kilpatrick had warned me about, Dr. Durand.

"What's that you say?" my patient screeched in the sudden silence.

The big doctor turned toward the noise, glared at me and bawled out in a voice worthy of a platoon sergeant, "Get that goddam cart out of here!"

"Yessir," I said. I was trembling with fright as I hastily wheeled my supply cart out of the ward.

"Now!" I heard the big voice boom behind me. "What do you intend to do with this patient, doctor?"

I was wiping the sweat off my forehead when Jennie wandered by. I grabbed her arm.

"Is that Durand?" I stage-whispered.

She peeked into the ward and a broad smile lit up her face. "The Red Devil!" she said, with obvious relish. "If you want some fun, Louanne, you just keep your ear glued to this door. Stay out of his way, mind you. But listen. He'll be telling off those smart-assed interns any moment now!"

"I never saw him before—"

"Well, you're seeing him now, baby. And for my money he's the best thing you're ever going to see around here! He may cuss you out and he may cuss me out. And he sure as hell is going to cuss out the doctors. But watch him. He's never going to cuss out those poor sick patients, that's for sure. . . . I gotta go now, Louanne. But you stay. You'll learn something, believe me!"

She hurried off down the corridor. Scared as I was, I decided to do just that. I tucked in against the side of the door, where I could run fast when they started out. But I was mighty curious to find out if what Jennie claimed was true. By now I'd had enough of some of those interns to like the idea of hearing them get theirs.

It wasn't hard to hear. There was something about Dr. Durand, I soon found, that inspired silence. Not only from the young doctors, but from the patients as well. He was so big and so strong that lesser people simply shut up and fell back before him.

I peeked around the door and saw that Dr. Durand had stopped beside the bed of an elderly woman with a hip cast on. He read the chart, turned to the intern in charge of the case and his big voice lashed across the silence of the room: "WHAT ARE YOU DOING ABOUT HER?"

The intern stepped timidly forward. "Well, I did have X-rays made, sir, and I think I'll take off the cast tomorrow or maybe next week."

Dr. Durand flipped the chart contemptuously. "Why not last week?" he demanded. "Turn her over."

When the nurse and intern got the old lady turned over so that the top of her hip cast was clearly visible from the back, Dr. Durand bent over her. As he examined her I could see his neck turn red, then his cheeks, finally the scalp beneath his blond hair.

He straightened up to his full height, looked down at the intern as though from some mountain top, and his voice was frigid with rage.

"You don't have to take the cast off, doctor," he announced icily. "You can just take the whole goddam leg off!" His long arm shot out in the air in a curiously accusing gesture that embraced the flock of young doctors. "How would you like to lose your leg—THROUGH SHEER NEGLIGENCE?"

Then he started swearing. The air got blue as the top of that poor old lady's leg. And the interns started scampering all over the ward.

They did get the cast off that same afternoon. And they did manage to save her leg from amputation. But

134

many times I was to see legs that were not saved because casts were left on—indefinitely—while old flesh was cut by the casts. X-rays were made, then stacked up and not read for a week or ten days—until it was too late.

As Grand Rounds continued, I faded back into the woodwork, watched them go by, and silently I tipped my cap to the Red Devil. He had scared me, but he could scare me a dozen more times if he liked—just so long as he kept up that big, loud lion's roar—on behalf of the patients. It was the first powerful voice I had heard in the patients' defense since I had started to work at the hospital.

Dr. Durand, I soon found, was the subject of much interest and speculation—as well as the cause for considerable fright—on the part of most of the staff. By all odds the most colorful doctor on the staff, he was also one of the most physically attractive. Yet he was so terrifying that none of the women—white or black —dared go near him. Serious, dedicated to his work, rough as a longshoreman in his speech, without a grain of frivolity or humor, he was not the sort of man any woman dared flirt with.

He also, I found, fit into the category that in my experience made for a compassionate doctor: he was poor. He was so poor, in fact, that he had started out as a lowly aide, even as I. From there he had scraped his way up, a step at a time, to the position he now held.

Most of our young doctors, both interns and residents, came from well-to-do upper middle-class families, and they just didn't seem to realize that poor people are human too. They treated the poor patients —and especially the non-white poor—with about the same degree of respect that they would a herd of cattle or a sty full of pigs. I was working in the male ward one morning when an intern called me to help him catheterize a Negro man. The doctor was smoking, and he didn't put down his cigarette, although we are supposed to take every precaution against contamination. I unwrapped the sterile gauze pack and placed it around the patient's penis. The doctor bent over the patient to insert the catheter, and some hot ashes from his cigarette fell on the man's penis. The patient jumped, and cried out. The doctor didn't even say "I'm sorry."

The doctors' indifference was so well-known in the ghetto that many sensitive people preferred to stay at home and die rather than expose themselves to such indignity.

I was back on the female ward a few days after my first meeting with Dr. Durand when I heard him coming again. Rather, I didn't hear him coming—it was the strange silence that preceded his appearance that alerted me. I finished tending my patient, then stood back quietly out of the way—at attention.

Dr. Durand strode into the ward, the flock of interns trailing him. He was, I noticed, the kind of man that puts each foot down like he knows exactly where he is going. He marched up to the bed of a patient who was in for gynecological observation, read her chart, and then turned on the intern who was caring for her.

136

"What are you going to do for her?" he demanded.

"I—I think I am going to remove her uterus, doctor," the intern said, "and perform a hysterectomy."

Dr. Durand glared at the young doctor, and when he spoke he didn't shout. His voice was low—and scalding.

"And just how would you like it for somebody to cut your nuts off?"

The intern flushed, looked at the floor, shifted his feet uncomfortably, and said nothing.

"You are talking about a woman, not a belly," Dr. Durand went on, his voice coldly polite, even formal, as he spelled out his lesson. "I would suggest that you work up this patient and find out if she really needs surgery or not." He paused a second to let his words sink in, then strode off to the next bed, the squadron of young doctors trailing him like frightened ducklings.

I felt like letting out a cheer. I had never before heard a staff doctor speak of a patient as other than a disease or a number.

I looked at those young doctors, wondering how much of what Dr. Durand said would sink in. God willing, some of it would. A few more giants like Dr. Durand, I thought, and we might produce a better crop of doctors—and a better hospital. I was sorry there wasn't one of him for each ward.

The aides were having coffee that afternoon when the call came in for two of us to report at once to the male surgical ward to receive three burn victims who had just been brought in by ambulance.

I was glad I already had my coffee down, to bolster

me. So far I had not been called on a burn case but I had heard the stories from the other aides. It was a duty everyone who could ducked out of, although our hospital got many burn cases each winter.

"Come on." Emma, a big, stout, older nurse's aide who had been at the hospital for at least ten years, grabbed my hand. "It's your turn."

When we reached the surgical ward, the burn victims were already there, on stretchers. I looked at the first stretcher helplessly. It was a man's body, and I suppose he was still alive, but the body was burned almost beyond recognition. The entire body surface was burned. There was no place to take hold of him. The stench was indescribable. The skin didn't look human; it looked like the skin of a chicken that has roasted too quickly—pieces of it were blown up in patches which, if you touched them with your cooking fork, would split and slip off the meat.

Ten or fifteen people—doctors, nurses, and ambulance attendants—were working around the stretchers. But it was up to Emma and me to get them into beds.

"Here, Louanne, grab hold of this." Emma had lifted the sheet from a bed and was smearing it with grease. "We have to grease the sheets so they won't pull more flesh off."

When we had the top and bottom sheets greased, she showed me how to roll the patient onto the sheet without taking a hand hold on him at any point, then roll him into the bed.

"Gently, gently," I heard a low voice behind me caution, "you can't know how painful that is."

Then I saw the now-familiar broad back walk past. It was Dr. Durand, come to check out the patients who would require surgery.

While the medical crew took over with the first man, we began on the second. When we had the three in bed, Emma and I stood a moment at the side of the ward, to catch our breath. "It's so sad," she muttered. "They work so hard to save these people—then they toss them right back into the same jungle to be burned again—"

"I don't think they are going to save these," I ventured. "There's not enough left of them."

"Just vegetables," Emma said. "Some of them die right away, some linger awhile, some get well—but if they do get well it takes six to eighteen months here, to do the skin grafts and all." She pointed to a patient, with a loop of skin growing from his face. "They get that started, to use to make the grafts."

"How can he sleep like that?" I asked, horrified.

"Oh, they manage," Emma said. "The burn patients console each other. Because no one else comes to see these people, and no one wants to work with them, they turn to each other, they are each other's psychiatrist, social worker, friend."

"Why do the workers avoid them?" I asked. "Just because it's so horrible to look at? Seems to me the cancer patients are as horrible—"

"It's the smell," Emma said. "Now you thought that smell of new-burned flesh was terrible, didn't you?"

"Yes," I admitted, "I had no idea—"

"Well, that's nothing compared to what those people will smell like in four or five days. It's so awful, I can't even tell you about it. If you don't have a strong stomach, you just start vomiting and never stop. The nurses and aides who do work in here have to use strong deodorizers to get near enough to these people to care for them. It's a shame too. Because the deodorizers are hard on the patients. After a while they do put them in a tub—it nearly kills the patients the first time they do it because it's all new skin—but once they have been bathed, they don't stink so much."

I thought of how many burn stories I had read in newspapers. "House burned, three injured." "Tenement swept by fire, toll fourteen dead, twenty hospitalized." I thought uneasily about my own boys in the apartment. It was very cold—it had already begun to snow—when I left for work that morning, and I had left a small heater on in the bathroom. I looked out the window; it was still snowing. If it got any heavier I might be late getting home. I decided to call home and ask Jim to wait till I got there before he left for his job. If he felt he had to leave, I told him to be sure and turn off the heater before he went.

Nothing I had ever read about burn victims had prepared me for what third and fourth degree burns actually look like. All the city hospitals get a large number of burn cases each winter—usually in the male ward. Sometimes whole families are caught in tenement fires, but more often it is the men who are badly burned, trying to save their wives and children. And we also get the firemen. Most of our cases come in on cold winter nights, and most of them are Negro. Many never survive the night they are brought to the hospital, because the burns cover so much of the body surface, and so much skin and tissue has been destroyed. Others are saved who would have been better off dead. They were alive and breathing, but that was all.

The burn patients that have large areas of their body surface destroyed are put into special wooden frame beds called Striker frames, which are constructed like a sandwich—two wooden frames with the patient in the middle. There is a wheel at the end of the bed and you can turn the patient completely over, just as you would flip a pancake. The doctors give them heavy sedation at first since burn patients are in such pain, so they sleep a lot of the time. Often they sleep face down, with their head in the hole that is cut in the frame so that they can breathe whichever way it is turned.

We had so many burn patients, that learning to turn those frames was a routine part of our training. Later, when I was moonlighting at a private hospital, I came across a burn patient who was in agony because he had not been turned in three days. The RN in charge had not been trained to handle a Striker frame and she was afraid to touch it.

Private hospital employees don't handle nearly the number of bodies that we do either. RNs who work in private hospitals have a saying: "Don't let the patient die on my shift." But there is no shift in a city hospital that doesn't see a death. We average ten deaths per day, year 'round. In winter, when in addition to the burn cases we get so many laboring men who don't come to us until they have collapsed from "walking pneumonia" or influenza, we may get as many as ten deaths on one ward.

Lester and I still worked together on the PMs. We had done so many by now we were fast and efficient and I preferred a man to a woman helper, particularly when we delivered the body to the morgue. I had never got over my first uneasy feeling about that sub-basement. They had lights down there, but they weren't bright enough and the passageway was always dim and spooky. I had got over what fear I had of the bodies, but I would not have wanted to go down to the morgue alone. The worst thing, for me, about going with Lester was that if it was late on our shift, and Ollie had come on duty, Lester always wanted to go by and chat with him before going back up to our floor. Lester had introduced me to Ollie once, and that was enough for me. He was a slippery con man type who had looked me over with that sly kind of smile that says, "I can gobble up ten little girls like you for breakfast." It's a look I know well, and I have never found it flattering. It makes me feel about as important as a dish of ice cream.

Lester and I brought a body down at the end of our shift one afternoon and got it rolled into a drawer in the morgue, when Lester suggested we drop by and visit Ollie in the furnace room.

"Not me," I said; I was impatient to start for home.

142

"It's nearly quitting time and I want to get home to my kids. With this snow, the buses are bound to be slow. Come on, Lester, let's go on back."

"Ah, you don't have to get home that fast," Lester wheedled. "Let's just stick our heads in the door—"

"You stick your head in," I said. "But hurry. I'll wait for you at the elevator."

I could see Lester was in an ornery mood and I wasn't going to change his mind, so I started back down the corridor from the morgue, toward the elevator, to wait for him there.

Lester headed in the opposite direction, down the dark hall toward the furnace room. Just to this side of it was a locker room for the hospital porters. I had nearly reached the elevator when I heard Lester gasp. I turned around. He had disappeared. Then I heard the click of the locker room door.

I wavered, frightened, wondering what to do. Go to find him? Call for help? Run away? I buzzed for the elevator. Maybe the operator could help me.

Then the door clicked a second time. I shrank back against the elevator door waiting. Two figures walked quickly from the locker room into the furnace room and disappeared. I remembered there was a service door in there. Even in the dim corridor, I recognized the uniforms of their profession: the dark glasses and silk suits. Each man carried a sawed-off shotgun. I raced down the hall to the locker room, bracing myself for what I would find there.

Lester and Ollie were still both very much alive,

143

but very shook up. Their faces were ashen with fear.

Ollie looked at me, his eyes black and somber. "It's a good thing you two came down just now." He shuddered. "If Lester hadn't walked in, I guess I'd have been your next body."

"Why did they let you go?" I asked.

"I promised I'd help Ollie pay up," Lester said. "If we can come through with the thousand he owes in a week, they'll let us off."

"A thousand dollars! How are you going to get a thousand dollars in a week?"

Lester shrugged. Ollie stared at his shoe.

"Why don't you tell the police?"

"Not me!" Lester said. "Baby, you don't know what they do. It's not just the man they get. They go after his family and friends too. I'm not telling anybody."

"But how can you get that kind of money?"

"We'll get it," Lester said in a flat voice. "We got to."

Neither of them would talk any more to me about it, so Lester and I went back up to our floor and I got my coat and purse to start home. But as I walked out into that dark, wintry afternoon I was chilled by more than the sharp, cold air. I considered going to the police myself. Then I discarded that thought. If Lester was telling the truth about how the syndicate worked —I couldn't have that on my conscience.

Ollie and Lester were in it. They would just have to get out by themselves.

CHAPTER *EIGHT*

What Is an Emergency?

The next day I was notified that I had been assigned to work two weeks on the twilight shift in the Emergency Room. I reported for duty the following afternoon.

It was four o'clock on a Saturday and the benches were overflowing with patients who had been waiting from one to five hours for a doctor to see them. One man was leaning against a wall, with a towel wrapped around his head, the blood dripping through it, down his neck and onto his blue work shirt. A woman was bent over holding her belly, obviously in labor, and screaming with pain. Another woman sat silently on the bench beside her, holding a child in a shawl in her arms. A junkie was climbing the wall, screaming and vomiting. Although it was wintertime and the corridors were not hot, the stench of blood and vomit filled the air and I realized that if you were fainty by nature you were long gone in this place.

"Nurse, nurse!" A gaunt, elderly man plucked at my skirt. "Can't you get me to the X-ray? I've been here five hours!"

"Bring me some water, will you, for my baby?" asked the woman holding the child. I glanced into the child's face. It was suspiciously still.

"You gotta get me to delivery—" The woman in labor tore at my arm with fingers tense with pain.

"I'll get the doctor—" I said helplessly, pulling away from them, hurrying down the hall, to check in for duty. It was obvious that to get anything done in this place you had to stay clear of that mob of suffering humanity.

As I reached the nurses' station, I heard the wail of the siren. The double doors flopped open, a stretcher was raced to emergency surgery. Two policemen ran interference alongside. The doors flipped again, a second stretcher was rushed down the corridor between the lanes of patients.

"Come on." The aide Emma, who was on duty, grabbed me. We followed the stretchers into adjoining cubicles. The two interns on duty began working on the first body. It was that of a young Puerto Rican. He was barely conscious but still breathing. I watched, fascinated, as the medical team expertly ripped away his clothing—exposed the gunshot wound in the shoulder. They worked over him no more than ten minutes, left him for us to clean up and deliver to the male ward, then rushed into the adjoining cubicle.

From the other side of the curtain, I heard one of the cops shouting at the second victim. "You know you're dying. Why in hell don't you tell us who shot you!"

"He won't say," Emma whispered to me. "This is one of those family feuds—probably was his own cousin—" She shook her head. "I used to think the Negroes were great for knives and guns. But these boys put us to shame. Stay around here a few more Saturday nights, Louanne, and you'll see whole families brought in, with stab wounds and gunshot. . . ."

"The cops aren't supposed to be in there, are they?" I asked. "Why don't the doctors make them go away?"

She shrugged. "Sometimes I think the cops and doctors feel the same about these people—they're just a nuisance to them—and they don't care if they are abused—"

She pulled a blood-encrusted stretcher from one side of the room; we loaded the man onto it.

"I'll wheel him upstairs. You might as well see if you can help the doctors in there."

There was no more sound from the other side of the screen.

When I had helped her get the stretcher out into the corridor and to the elevator, I walked back to the second cubicle.

The victim lay there on the examining table, completely naked and stone dead. His slender arms were spread helplessly at his sides, abandoned in death. No one had even bothered to pull the sheet over him. The doctors had apparently been working on him when he died, so they simply rushed off to the next patient, leaving him lying as he was. I felt a flush of anger as I thought of the last words this boy had heard on this earth: the shrill bark of an angry policeman telling him he was dying. What right did that lousy cop have to pronounce death to this man? What right had he to be in there at all, where a man lay dying?

I leaned over the boy a second, looking into the handsome young face, so pale and still in death. Then I pulled the sheet gently over him, saying a small prayer as I did it.

Emergency, I quickly found, is always swarming with cops. They get to the scene of the accident first; they accompany the victim in the ambulance. Unfortunately, some of them have read a medical article or two and fancy themselves as doctors. They are most dangerous in obstetrical emergencies. One white ghetto cop I know goes around bragging about the number of babies he has delivered. He even carries a little black bag with rubber gloves and clamps. Unless the baby's head is actually emerging from the mother's body, there is always time to get her to the hospital and professional care. But the cop likes the excitement, and if another black baby or black mother dies, who's to care?

The Emergency Room of a city hospital is the human garbage pail for all the malpractice, misjudgment

148

and abandonment that occurs in the city. It is also the "Ghetto Doctor." Few ghetto residents have private physicians. Those that do can't get their doctors out to make house calls after dark, because they are afraid of being mugged. So the ER serves as "doctor" not only for the victims of poison and accident that turn up in private hospital ERs, but also we get the cases that would be handled by a private physician in middle-class society: pneumonia, influenza, bungled abortion, the junkies. . . .

Many of our patients have already been turned down at Emergency Rooms of private hospitals, usually for financial reasons, and are carted across town and dumped on us. Often they are dead on arrival. It is supposed to be a part of medical ethics that patients are not to be moved when they are in shock. That first night I was on duty, Emma and I unloaded three women in shock who were hemorrhaging from incomplete abortions and had been sent to us from private hospitals. We also received a stretcher with a patient who had a needle taped to his arm and a bottle on a portable rack over his head—like a soldier being delivered from a front line first aid station to the base hospital.

I couldn't believe it. "You mean some doctor took the trouble to get the intravenous started—and *then* kicked the patient out?" I asked.

Emma laughed. It was a grim little sound. "Guess that doctor got religion—and didn't want this poor fellow to die on the way here!"

I had read my medical textbook and I still couldn't get over it. "But a doctor's not supposed to do that."

"Listen, honey," she said. "We get everything—because this is the end of the line. We don't turn down *anybody*. Not the abortions, nor the junkies, nor the cats who get knifed every Saturday night. We take 'em all. And those other hospitals, they know it. So they take one look—and if the victim doesn't look like he's good for compensation they toss him over to us. This place may look like a butcher shop—but you'd be surprised how many folks we take care of that get well."

I was amazed at how many pieces of humanity came through Emergency that night. Ambulances screamed to the door every five or ten minutes. Bodies were rushed in on stretchers. Patients were sutured, patched together, revived—fifty, a hundred—just like some enormous factory churns out bolts of material. You didn't dare stop running or even look closely at any one of the patients—let alone learn their names. One slow-down in Emergency could easily mean a death. And when the surgery rooms weren't full, we called out numbers, and let the bench warmers (who had been judged not critical) come in one at a time. Twice when I called a number, there was no answer and when I went out to the benches, I found the patient on the floor. It's not unusual, Emma told me, after sitting there for four, five, or six hours, for the patients to faint.

Yet, somehow, we continued to get them treated,

and turn them out. Something we could not give them was a spot to sit, and recover, following treatment. If the patient was not considered in sufficiently serious conditon to be admitted to a ward, he or she was simply dismissed after treatment to find his way home as best he could. The patients stumbled out onto the street, and if they had the money, they looked for a cab. If not, they headed for the subway station four blocks away.

Around five-thirty I saw a neatly dressed middle-aged woman come in and take a place on the bench, and I thought of something Emma had told me: "Any time you see a good coat in ER, you can bet they are scared." Patients who could afford nice clothes only turned up at city ER rooms when they become suddenly ill, and couldn't find their own doctors. What with the surgical emergencies, it was two hours before a doctor could see her. When her number came up I took her into one of the cubicles. The doctor came in, examined her for a few minutes, then shook his head.

"I can't find a thing wrong with you. Go home."

"But I feel so strange," she said, her eyes bright with fear. "Please, doctor, could I stay here awhile? I just don't feel like going home—"

"There's no need for you to stay here, really," the doctor insisted. "You do not have a temperature. You might just as well go home." He walked away to the next examining room, and the next patient. "If you still feel bad tomorrow, go to the clinic."

She stared after him, moistened her lips as if to

speak, then decided against it. Slowly she gathered up her coat and purse and started out to the reception room. There was something about her face that made me follow.

"Why don't you let me try to find a bench or stretcher somewhere?" I asked. "You could rest a few moments before you start out."

"No, no thank you," she shook her head. "I'll just go on home, like the doctor said."

I said goodnight, and started back to the examining rooms, then something prompted me to stop, turn and check to see if she had made it all right. I watched as she pulled the heavy door open, walked outside. The door swung slowly shut behind her. She started down the steps. And then her whole body went down. I ran outside. She was crumpled on the steps, her face down. I turned it gently—looked into the staring eyes. She was dead.

The autopsy revealed that she had suffered a coronary. The doctor had missed this in his diagnosis. But that was not why I hated him. It was because he had refused to listen to her. Or acknowledge the fear in her eyes. He had shown her no compassion, and, instead, had sent her out to find her way home alone. We could have kept her. I could have found a bed somewhere—rather than turn her out after she had pleaded with us to stay.

What we really needed was an observation or recovery room next door to Emergency, some place where we could put those people who were shaky or frightened, where they could get a night's sleep, and then, after eight hours if they seemed in good shape, go home. Or, if they indeed proved ill, we could transfer them to a ward. Of course it would cost the city another bit of floor space and another attendant, but it could make all the difference in humanity.

There was no one free to go with me when I took her body down to the morgue. Emma helped me get it onto the elevator, then rushed back to Emergency to get the woman in labor up to OB before she delivered on the waiting bench.

I dreaded going down there by myself. The basement, Ollie, and then those black-suited boys had me really psyched up to the point that if I did have to go I made the quickest flight you ever saw. If there was no one else on the elevator, I asked the operator to wait for me, and I hurried down to the morgue, left the body, raced back to the elevator, and sighed with relief when I once again reached light and air—and safety.

Tonight the operator had three lights flashing on his call board by the time we reached the subbasement.

"Sorry, Louanne," he told me. "I can't wait for you. I'll be back soon's I can."

The elevator door clanked shut behind me. I peered down the corridor, as though expecting the black suits to materialize again, but there was no one in sight. I hurried down to the morgue, left the body, and had just stepped back into the corridor and closed the door behind me, when I heard my name called.

153

"Louanne! Where have you been? Come on in."

It was Ollie, leaning against the doorway of the furnace room. I suppose he had heard my footsteps in the hall. I was surprised to see him so relaxed.

"No thanks, Ollie," I said quickly. "They're waiting for me upstairs. I was transferred."

"Where are you now?"

"ER."

"Emergency!—Well!" He walked over to me, put his hand on my arm. His voice was low and confidential. "Baby, that's the very best scene you could get!"

"What do you mean?" I paused, captured. I didn't like Ollie and I definitely didn't like his hand on my arm. But I was curious what he meant.

He glanced around quickly to see if anyone was coming. The corridor was empty. "Listen, baby," he said quickly, "anyone who works Emergency can write the best book in the building."

I pulled away from his hand. "You expect me to write numbers for the patients?" I was annoyed.

"Man, yes!" Ollie whistled. "What a setup. All those cats lined up there, just sitting and waiting, with nothing to do. Honey, you can make a killing—"

"Not me, Ollie," I said. "I've got enough to do."

He looked disappointed. "You're a fool to pass up an easy buck like that. Emergency's the greatest spot in the hospital for digits—and booze."

"I think it's awful to give those sick people liquor!" I said sharply, "—before we even know what's wrong with them. It could do them a lot of harm."

"Oh, honey," Ollie laughed, "you are really the

squarest chick around. I can't get over you, I really can't!—and not bad-looking either." His eyes lazed over my body. "If you don't cotton to digits or booze, you might make out in the doctor's dining room—"

"What are you talking about?" I asked, puzzled. I never had heard that one.

"Go see the lady that runs the dining room," Ollie suggested. "They always put the prettiest aides in there to wait on the doctors. Then the doctors and the girls, they can work it out from there. But a lot of goodlooking chicks pick up pin money, or just good times, whichever they like—"

"Thanks, Ollie, but I'd just as soon work for mine," I walked over to the elevator and pushed the button. "I haven't had to go out whoring yet, and I'm not about to begin. I'm not a kitchen aide any more, either," I said proudly. "I'm learning to be a nurse!"

"The nurses do it too, baby," Ollie laughed. "You don't need to feel so high and mighty!"

I didn't bother to answer that. Ollie was the kind of man who always got the last—dirty—word. He had all the vices going for him, and he dearly loved to make me seem stupid.

"You're looking pretty cool," I said, "for a man whose time is running out. When's your due date—tomorrow?"

"Aw, don't worry," Ollie said easily. "We rounded up a little cash, and did a little talking and we got—what's that fancy name for it"—he rolled his eyes—"stay of execution? That's what we got."

"For how long?" I asked him.

"Another week."

I got on the elevator, wondering how he could be so easy about the whole thing. As for me, I'd rather work for an honest living, and I had a hunch I'd be around this world a lot longer than Ollie would.

I just didn't have a clue how very short his time was running.

I got back up to ER just as a young Negro girl was being brought in from the ambulance on a stretcher. As usual, there was a cop running alongside. But there was something about this one that caught my attention. He was a stocky, powerfully built man, but he wasn't pushing his weight around or acting arrogant like most of the cops did. He wasn't giving any orders to anyone, and he kept glancing down at the girl with a look of real concern on his handsome black face.

"She's awful sick," he said to me when he saw that I was watching him. "She should have called for help before now."

"We'll take care of her," I promised, as the nurse and I wheeled the stretcher to an examining room. The cop nodded, with a look of relief, then stepped politely back out of our path. I gave him a big smile as I brushed by. I liked the idea that there were still some men like him around, who hadn't forgot their manners, nor where their heart was.

Inside the examining room, the nurse laid back the sheet. The stench was overpowering. The girl was hemorrhaging from an incomplete abortion, but she had been untended so long that a thick green discharge indicated severe infection had set in. Her face

156

was pinched with pain, her eyes closed, her pulse thready. Without immediate drastic medical procedures, she was obviously, as the compassionate cop had noticed, near death.

Two of the young interns who were on duty strode in, made a quick examination, and then one of them told me to take her on up to the female ward and get her to bed, and they would follow.

I had just found a bed for her, when the two young doctors appeared. They both examined her. Then one of them said to her.

"Okay, who did it?"

The girl turned her face away and didn't answer.

"Tell us who did it," the doctor repeated sternly. "Where did you get your abortion?"

She made no reply.

He leaned over her. "Now listen to me. We are going to let you lie here and die unless you tell us who did it."

She turned to him then, with a look of pure hate. But she still said nothing.

"You better tell us," the other doctor chimed in. "We are not going to do anything for you until you do."

The girl did not answer.

The doctors left the ward. I followed them to the door.

"What should I do for her?"

"Nothing," one of them told me, "until she decides to talk. Then you can call us."

They walked off down the corridor.

I went back to the girl's bed. I took her hand in mine, and forced her to look at me.

"Listen," I whispered to her, "all you have to do is say a name—any name. Say you went to Canada for the abortion. Tell them anything that comes in your head. But *say something*, so we can take care of you."

She shook her head silently, and turned her face to the wall.

I looked at her, feeling helpless. Her eyes were shut, her face young and unguarded. She was a small, pretty girl—not more than twenty years old. Surely somebody cared whether she died. . . .

Then I thought of someone who might care. Dr. Durand, the Red Devil. The thought of going to him scared me, but I remembered his words: "This is a woman, doctor, not a belly. . . ."

He would listen to me. I went outside, found the charge nurse and asked her where his room was. Luckily, he was still at the hospital.

I went in, and spoke my piece quickly with no preliminaries. "There's a newly admitted abortion case in Room 7, on the female ward, doctor, who appears to be dying from infection. The doctors who examined her refused to begin treatment until she tells them who did it."

He gave me a quick, sharp look, then said, "I'll be right up."

I went back to the female ward to wait. Dr. Durand appeared within five minutes. He examined the girl; immediately ordered intravenous infusions started.

158

She survived. No thanks to that pair of sadists who examined her first. Whether or not Dr. Durand called the younger doctors on the carpet for their inhuman neglect, I will never know. There was certainly no noticeable change in their, or the other doctors', attitude toward the abortion victims.

I could never understand why so many men were so vicious and cruel about abortion. The same young doctors or cops who would be the first to advise their own sweethearts to find an abortion rather than face a scandal, treated all the hospital abortion cases like a bunch of sluts. Many of these women were actually decent married women who were either too weak from other pregnancies, or too poor to face another delivery. The tragedy of the ghetto is that so many women attempt to abort themselves. With no medical knowledge, they assume all they have to do is stick something sharp up there and they use everything from straightened coat hangers to knitting needles, and often puncture the uterus. One woman had to have emergency abdominal surgery to flush her organs of the turpentine with which she had saturated herself internally. Many women who butcher themselves die at home because they are too proud and too frightened to come to the hospital.

Late that night, only minutes before I was to go off duty, the sirens wailed again, the ambulance door burst open, and a small army of shouting, crying, praying Spanish people burst upon us. It was the result of a car wreck—and as to how many of these people were actually victims, and how many merely distraught relatives who had piled into the ambulance with them, it took several minutes to figure out. While we were trying to sort out the melee, a tiny Indian doctor who was on duty spotted a huge, elderly woman among the victims who was already in cardiac arrest.

Since she needed emergency heart massage that instant and the floor offered a better flat surface for her ponderous bulk than a normal examining table, the little doctor, who couldn't have weighed over ninety pounds, made the heroic gesture: He tackled her, threw her to the floor, jumped astride her and began administering heart massage manually.

Before any one of us realized what was about to happen, one of the woman's male Puerto Rican relatives, mistaking the intent of our brave little doctor, made a flying tackle at him, and started beating on his back and trying to pull him off the victim.

Then Emma went into action, grabbed a male aide, and me, and the three of us went for the relative and dragged him off the doctor before he had done much damage.

"What we really need around here," Emma grunted, "is a translator!"

When I finally walked out of the hospital gate late that night, a figure moved out of the shadows, and walked toward me. It was Lester.

"So where have you been hiding?" I asked, nastily. He hadn't been at work for several days that I knew of.

160

"Listen, Louanne," Lester's voice was low and urgent and he didn't even pretend to smile. "It's my hide or my job, and my hide is more important. I can't come back till we're all paid off."

"Then it doesn't look like you've got a job here any more," I was feeling pretty snappish about the whole business. It had been Ollie's problem, not his, and I thought Lester was a fool to have got in it. "You'll just have to stay in hiding, I guess."

"No, you're wrong, Louanne," Lester argued, trailing alongside me as I walked toward my bus stop. "We got most all we need. Another twenty-five or thirty bucks and we'll be off the hook. Loan me ten, will you, baby? I'll pay you back next week—"

"*Ten dollars*! Are you kidding? Ten dollars will buy my kids groceries for a week."

"You gotta help me, Louanne," Lester pleaded. "Just this once. I'll get it back to you—and more, I promise. If I can just put together this last bit, then I can come back to work and everything'll be fine again. I want to come back, Louanne. I've missed you. . . ."

"I haven't got ten dollars, Lester," I told him. But I felt myself weakening. If they really were that close to paying off and being done with it, I hated to think Lester would get beaten up just because I wouldn't let him have a few dollars. "I'll loan you two dollars."

"Make it five, baby. Just five, please!" Lester begged, his voice brightening with hope.

Reluctantly, I opened my pocketbook, and slowly counted out five ones, feeling as guilty while I did it as though I was taking the bread right out of my little boys' mouths.

"Oh, thanks, baby, thanks!" Lester grabbed the bills out of my hand and was off and running. "I'll make it up to you—honest," he yelled over his shoulder, as he disappeared around the block.

I went home, feeling like a fool. I didn't tell Sis or Clarice or anyone what I'd done. But I made up my mind, that once the heat was off Ollie and Lester I'd find a way to get my money back.

CHAPTER NINE

The Man Acts

Although Dr. Durand served no official capacity at the Emergency Room, I was glad to see that it did not entirely escape his critical attention. At least once every other day he suddenly appeared, without warning, striding through the corridors, setting the staff flying like frightened chickens, poking his big handsome head into each cubicle.

"What's that woman lying there for? Why hasn't she been sent up to the ward?"

"Who's taking care of this patient? Why hasn't he been sutured?"

"Where the hell are the doctors?"

Even the pleading, plaintive patients fell back silently when he strode past. It wasn't just a matter of being cowed by him, either. Like a big, sturdy captain walking through the ship during a storm, Dr. Durand's presence promised security and help. He never spoke to me again about the girl he had saved. Not that I expected him to. He might cuss out the interns to their faces, but he was not about to discuss their behavior with an aide.

Nor did he smile when he saw me. But he looked at me—that straightforward, piercing look of his—and the slight, stiff dip of his head was evidence he recognized my face. I knew that if I had to go to him again I would not be turned away.

During the weekdays, Emergency, I found, varied from a handful of patients to forty or fifty. It was Saturday nights that the place was chaos, when all the victims of weekend auto accidents, party fights, were hauled in. My second Saturday on Emergency, I dragged home at midnight, exhausted, and went straight to bed. My brother Jim was still out playing poker with friends of his. Sunday when I got up I was surprised to find Jim's bed in the hall bedroom was still empty. Midafternoon when I was ready to leave for the hospital, he still hadn't appeared. When I reached Emergency, I soon found out why. The whole poker party had been brought in about an hour after I left the night before, and they had all been treated, then put to bed in the male ward.

The story, as I pieced it out later, was that one of the men had lost a lot of money, and when the others were ready to break up the game, he wanted to go on playing so he could get his money back. When the other three players refused, the loser pulled a gun and started shooting. He was aiming wildly and he winged one fellow in the shoulder, another in the arm.

He got my brother in the hip. But Jim is a big, strong, tough man and one bullet in the hip didn't keep him down. He was so mad at the bad loser that he hobbled out to the kitchen, got a cast iron frying pan and belabored the gunman around the head with it until the cops, who had been called by the neighbors, hauled him off. All four were loaded up and sent to Emergency.

I hurried up to the male ward to see Jim. To my horror, I found that all four poker players had been given beds together in one small room. I greeted Jim, then rushed out to find the supervisor. By the looks of my brother—and the other men—I felt the danger was by no means passed.

"Don't keep those four men in one room," I warned her. "They were all in a fight together and they'll be at each other again."

"But they are all wounded," the nurse said. "They can't get out of their beds."

"Maybe the others can't," I told her, "but my brother can. He isn't hurt so bad he can't get out of bed and walk—and he is still mad. And if he gets mad enough he just may walk over to that other bed and choke that fellow with his bare hands!"

"All right," the nurse nodded, apparently convinced I wasn't kidding. She didn't want that kind of scene, either. "We'll separate them."

"Thanks," I said. "But promise you'll do it *now.*" I went back down to Emergency.

With Jim temporarily in the hospital, Clarice couldn't resist showing her true nature. Sis had always claimed that Clarice and her sister Loula had me fooled with all their church-going and song-singing, and that they were both a pair of tarts where men were concerned (the story went that Clarice worked part time at the hospital in order to drum up business with the doctors, and Loula was really screwing around with their preacher) but I wouldn't listen, because I liked them both, and I don't go around clucking over other women's morals. This time, however, Clarice managed to rub my nose in it.

She was staying nights with me, while Jim was in the hospital, to help me watch my kids, while Loula was watching hers. The old woman who lived on the top floor of our building had a young, good-looking nephew visiting her at this time. We had all met him, but I hadn't thought much about it one way or another because ever since I'd become a grown woman I never cared about pretty boys, other than to look at. But I guess this one looked so good to Clarice she just had to have a little. I was getting ready for bed the next night, and when I went around the apartment to lock up, I didn't see Clarice anywhere. She was staying in the hall bedroom and the door was closed so I decided she must have already gone to sleep. I found that the hall window that opened onto the fire escape was open a little, so I locked it, and went to bed. Around one A.M. I was wakened by a funny little tapping sound. I listened a moment, got up, and followed the sound to the fire escape window. Clarice was crouched outside on the fire escape. I opened the window and let her in, and didn't make any comment, although it was clear enough why I'd found the window unlocked in the first place.

Nor did I carry any tales to my brother. He was mad enough as it was without hearing about her. By the time he did get out of the hospital, Clarice was pregnant. She tried to hang it on Jim, but he wasn't buying any of that. Instead, he simply cut out of her life for ever, and started looking for another girl.

When it was clear she wasn't going to get Jim back, Clarice decided not to have that baby. Next thing I knew she wasn't pregnant any more and I didn't ask her how she got rid of it because abortions were common as mud in the community and I made it my business not to find out about them. The results of the unsuccessful ones were all too evident at the hospital. But Clarice was a lucky girl and nothing more happened to her physically than that she was no longer pregnant. Emotionally she was in worse trouble. I guess she had her heart set on that young man and the night he announced his engagement to a girl his own age I got an emergency call from his aunt:

"Come upstairs quick. Clarice is committing suicide!"

I dashed upstairs and there was Clarice pouring a bottle of merthiolate down her throat while the old aunt moaned and groaned. Clarice was rolling her eyes, and the liquid was running down the sides of her mouth and it looked bad. All I could think of was "Butter!"

I dashed back down to my apartment. Sis had lucked into a good temporary job that week and she had bought a whole pound of honest-to-God butter, like we used to get on the farm. I opened the refrigerator, grabbed the butter, and ran back upstairs and started shoving it down Clarice—to counteract the poison—while I told the old lady to call for an ambulance.

When Sis saw me run out with her pound of butter, she followed me. I was cramming it into Clarice's mouth when Sis came on the scene. Sis has always been a cool one and she sized up just how much of that merthiolate was coming out of the sides of Clarice's mouth and how much actually had gone into her throat, and Sis knew it was a fake suicide.

"You give me back my frigging butter!" she yelled at me. "What do you mean feeding it to that damn whore?"

By then the ambulance had arrived and they hauled Clarice off to the hospital. And sure enough, Sis was right. Clarice had no intention of killing herself and she hadn't swallowed over a quarter teaspoonful of that stuff—not enough to burn her throat, let alone her stomach. Of course the pound of butter was ruined. And Sis didn't quit cussing me out about it for a month.

Sis and I were always squabbling about something. We were probably closer to each other than to anyone else in the world but it was the kind of closeness that meant we always had some kind of running argument. I really did miss her, later that year, when she married and moved into an apartment of her own. But we were not to be separated for long. Since she had been North, Sis had tried a number of different jobs, and she was such a good cook that I really expected her to end up running a little restaurant of her own. Instead, to my surprise, she decided to join me at the hospital and study to become a practical nurse. It was a lucky day for a lot of patients when she made that decision. She has that just-right balance of cool nerve and compassion that makes the best nurse.

When I came out of my door, the very next day after Clarice's hokey suicide, to go to work, I saw one of the hospital ambulances drive up in front of a rooming house across the street, next door to where Clarice and her sister lived. Being nosy, I yelled over to the attendant to find out who it was he had come for.

"Police call to pick up twin babies," he told me.

I hurried over. I didn't know my neighbors across the street. It was a dilapidated six-floor frame building; I had seen the tenants coming and going, and I remembered the young, skinny, poor-looking Negro mother whom I had seen wheeling a broken-down carriage with two babies in it. All I knew about her was that she obviously had neither a job nor a husband.

I showed the attendant my hospital pass and went with him into the building. The front hall was dank and stinking, the wooden stairs were rotting away.

"Third floor," he told me.

We climbed up, around piles of garbage, paper, and chunks of falling plaster. At the third floor, the cop was waiting for us.

"In here," he said quietly. His voice was so sub-dued I stared at him. It was that same nice-looking Negro cop who had brought in the abortion case. He looked sick.

He pointed, silently, to the bare wood table in the center of the room. On it was a cardboard box with the babies inside. One of them was lying very still and blue, obviously dead; the other was still alive and cry-ing a thin little meeuw like a sick kitten. I looked closer at the live one and almost lost my breakfast. The baby had had a bowel movement since he had been lying there untended, and flies had got into it and bred maggots. The maggots were all over the baby's body. They had eaten into the tender flesh of his belly, legs and throat.

The attendant simply picked up the box and we carried the whole mess to the hospital as it was. There the dead baby was prepared for the morgue; the live one was given emergency treatment and then sent up to the nursery. I went up to visit the baby each day that he was with us, just to make sure he was still alive. Miraculously he did survive. The flesh finally healed over and he gained weight and within six weeks he was well enough to be transferred to a foundling home. I don't know what happened to the mother. She never came back to her apartment and I never saw her again.

If she intended to desert her babies, she should have brought them to us in the first place. Many ghetto women do. A woman will come into ER with a baby in a shawl and the nurse and doctor will take it to an examining room to treat, and then when they bring it back, the mother has disappeared. She knows that the hospital will put the baby in a foundling home where at least it won't die of malnutrition.

That afternoon I was escorting a patient to the door of the Emergency receiving room when a couple of white grade school kids burst through the door. I paused, wondering what they wanted. Seeing my uniform, they ran to me.

"Come help, our friend's hurt!"

They dragged me out the door with them, across the street to the playground of the school that lies across from the hospital. I let them drag me along, because I had learned long ago that when kids think there's an emergency, there usually is. But when we rushed into the schoolyard, I couldn't see anything wrong. Other children were playing games. There was no one lying on the ground.

Then they led me up to the boy. He was a fat child, standing absolutely immobile, holding his thigh so tightly with both hands that the leg below his rolled blue jeans was chalk white.

"He cut his leg," explained one of the kids. "He was riding his bike through the cut in the fence and he got caught on the wire."

I still had seen no blood. "Let go," I said gently to the boy. "Let me see the cut."

The boy unclenched his hands. A wall of blood

171

gushed down the inside of his blue jeans, filled his shoe and puddled out onto the ground.

"Don't look," I told him hastily. I sent one of the boys back, on the run, to the hospital, for the ambulance. While we waited I applied pressure to stop the bleeding. The child's leg was laid open to the bone from the hip to the knee—the flesh was cut as cleanly as though a butcher had cut steaks.

The ambulance picked him up and I went with him back to the Emergency room. We had him sutured in no time, and he was soon back on the playground with his friends—although he didn't try riding through that cut in the wire fence again. It was a cut which the boys themselves had made so that they could ride through, but this little fellow was too fat to make it.

After that the little boys in the block "knew me." It gave me a kick to have them yell and wave at me every time I walked past their playground.

There's always some kind of crowd in the block in front of the hospital, what with the school across the street, and the hospital workers, and patients coming in, and all the visitors we have coming to see the patients. I was on my way to work a few days later, walking from my bus stop which is on the same side of the street as the hospital, when I saw a woman come out of the visitors' entrance to the hospital, hesitate at the curb, then step out into the street without really looking at the oncoming traffic. She was obviously distraught, and hadn't judged carefully and she might have made it—except that one oncoming car was traveling too fast to stop. It was awful. Just like one of those slow-motion movies. I saw her step out. I saw the car coming fast. And then there was her body, sailing up into the air, just like a piece of paper that's been caught in the wind.

I ran to her. But the school kids were faster than I was and by the time I reached her side, one of the boys was trying to hold her up.

"No, don't do that!" I called to him. I knelt beside her and eased her back down onto the street, laid my coat over her and told them to run for our ambulance. There was no reason to look for identification; I figured we would load her, and her purse, into the ambulance, and find out all those things later.

She was a white lady, probably about sixty years old. I was still on my knees beside her when another white woman, who must have seen the accident from her apartment window, shouldered her way through the crowd of kids.

"What did you do with her purse?" she demanded of me, her voice accusing.

I looked up at her. "Not a damn thing," I said. "It's right there." I pointed to the handbag, lying beside the woman. "No one has touched it."

"Well," the woman said, eying me, "I'll take it and keep it for her."

I looked her over, and I didn't like her or what she was insinuating. There's a kind of white person who automatically figures "all niggers are thieves." "Why should you?" I asked her. "You didn't come out here to help this woman. You came for her purse."

"Well, I want to keep it for her so nothing will get stolen," she had the nerve to say.

I could have slapped her. But I did not know how to keep the purse away from her. "Take it if you want," I told her. "But you just be sure *you* don't take anything out of it. Because I'm reporting this to the police, and I'm going to tell them you have her purse!"

She took it anyway. I did report to the police that she had it, which may have kept her from taking anything. The victim had internal injuries, but she did survive. And I guess she eventually got her purse back.

That's one trait of human nature—white and black —that's hard to understand, but more common than any one of us would like to believe. I once gave emergency care to a diabetic who passed out in front of a store, and I was working with her when I happened to look around in time to see one of those young, flashy Dapper Dan black boys getting into her purse. When I told him to leave it alone, he claimed he was "looking for her identification." I knew what he was looking for and it wasn't any identification. I made him put it down. It's in the same class as grave-robbing as far as I'm concerned. But wherever you find a helpless victim, you also find somebody who tries to get his purse or wallet.

The worst thieves are the junkies. If you have to support a thirty- or forty-dollar-a-day habit, you've got hot fingers for anything that converts to cash. When I first started working at the hospital, we had our share of junkies, but it's nothing to what we get

174

today, when fifty percent of our Emergency Room patients are on drugs, regardless of what brings them to the hospital. Yet, there are still no narcotics facilities at our hospital. The addict who turns up in our Emergency Room is at the individual mercy of whatever doctor examines him. Some doctors have enough humanity in their souls to prescribe drugs, and bring the addicts off with relatively little agony. Others are as contemptuous of addicts as they are of the abortion victims.

Many addicts die in the street, and arrive at our hospital DOA. The ones that we do revive often have other complications. We got one Puerto Rican kid that week—he couldn't have been more than nineteen—who had contracted pneumonia. The doctor who examined him prescribed cold turkey to take him off drugs before we treated him for pneumonia. It was really pathetic, to watch that boy going through withdrawal. He was absolutely wild, climbing the walls. We put him in the medical ward, and it took four of us to hold him down while we tied his feet and legs. He was just like an animal, and he'd break out as soon as we got the restraints on, screaming and raving, begging and crying. I couldn't believe anyone would let another human being suffer like that. But I guess the doctor was a moralist. He said cold turkey, and that's what he meant. Finally the boy got one hand free, and snatched up a glass urinal before I could get it away from him, broke it, then started waving the broken glass around, ready to fight. There were four of us assigned to him, which was an awful waste of personnel, and we begged the doctor to give him something so he wouldn't be so dangerous. He finally did give him enough Demerol so that he passed out.

Few white doctors will thank me for saying so, I'm sure, but the most successful treatment of narcotics addicts that I have observed in the ghetto is conducted by the Black Muslims. Under the leadership of Malcolm X they worked out an addiction-treatment program that is very much like AA and, like AA, demands dedicated work from its members. To begin with: Like Malcolm X himself, the Muslims who help addicts have to have "been there" before they can win the trust of the addicts. Then they work with them weeks or months, depending on the individual, until the addict admits he is one, and understands why. Then when they get him psyched up to do it, he voluntarily chooses cold turkey, under the constant aid and inspiration of the Muslim ex-junkies who speak his language and know every ache and agony he's going through. Once he has kicked the monkey off his back, the ex-addict keeps up his newfound self-respect and inspiration by going back among his junkie friends on the streets and fishing out one of them and working with him.

There's a vicious cycle about drugs. There's always somebody up there who's rich, who makes addicts out of the poor. Then, the poor, in order to support such an expensive habit, prey upon the rich. And round and round it goes. One of the reasons for the Black Muslims' success with addicts is that they point this out. "Don't make Whitey any richer by buying his dope, and killing yourself!" is what they preach. The answer, just like AA's answer, is to build up personal pride. If you learn to value yourself as a human being you don't need to escape reality.

As my second week on Emergency service drew to a close I realized I had not seen Lester since the night he borrowed the five dollars. On Friday, which was payday, the Cadillac limousines and the black-suited boys were outside the hospital gates at their usual stands, waiting to make their collections. I wondered if Ollie and Lester had succeeded in raising all the money they needed. I knew they had both been shaking down all their friends around the hospital, but I had not seen either one of them all week. I guess they figured that five was all they could hope to get out of me.

On Sunday I had a nice half day at home before I went to work. I took the kids to church, while Sis cooked a big midday dinner for us. I was feeling full and relaxed and happy when I reached the hospital gate that afternoon, and saw Lester standing there, in the shadow of the fence. His face was haggard, his eyes seemed focused on something beyond my shoulder that only he could see. When he spoke, his voice trembled.

"They got him, Louanne," he said softly. Even then he didn't look at me. His eyes reminded me of those newspaper pictures of soldiers who had been in battle too long—staring, not seeing.

"Ollie?"

"Yeah. This morning."

"How?"

Lester winced, shook his head roughly as though to clear it. "Remember that freight elevator in the basement? The one we don't use on Sundays? Well, somebody noticed it was stuck this morning. So—we took a look to see what was wrong. His body was in it. —Just the body, Louanne. There was no head."

Lester swallowed, then his voice dragged on. "We—we found the head later, down by his office, rolling around on the floor. They had put a bunch of empty liquor bottles around to make it look like he'd got drunk, then caught himself in the door of the freight elevator—"

"What about you, Lester?" I asked. "Why didn't they get you, too?"

"I'd paid up," Lester said. "But Ollie was in deeper than he let on. He owed The Man, too, and he was trying to hold out some for him. That's why they did it like that, as a warning to the rest of us." Lester looked down at his shoes for a moment, then took a long, slow breath. "I'm going home now, Louanne. And sleep—if I can. But I wanted you to know—"

His voice trailed off as he walked away. I waited a moment but he didn't turn around and he didn't look back.

178

CHAPTER *TEN*

Billy Gets a Daddy

The official report of Ollie's death was based on the circumstantial evidence. He had been drinking on the job, and while drunk had attempted to run the service elevator, had slipped, and accidentally been decapitated. Of course none of the hospital employees who knew Ollie believed that garbage for a moment. They knew who got him. They knew why. And they knew that the particularly ghoulish form of death was deliberate warning to the rest of us not to try any of Ollie's smooth tricks.

After Ollie's death, the syndicate apparently took the heat off Lester because he soon got over his shock, reported regularly for work, and seemed to be his gay old flirty self. Lester did not appear the least bit worried. But I was. I wanted my five dollars back. Besides, I had caught Lester in so many lies by now I realized he was nothing but bad news for anyone, and I had decided not to have so much as a cup of coffee with him again. I regretted the few times I had, because I found out that he had spread the story around that my husband wasn't coming back, and he was going to write him for a divorce, and take care of me and my children himself. Which was exactly the opposite of the truth. The last letter I had from Judson said that his sister finally had died, and as soon as he had cleared up the details for his mother in the South, he would be on a train north to join us. When I told Billy his Daddy was coming home, he could hardly contain himself. It had been four years since he'd seen him, and while my brother Jim had been a pretty good substitute father for him, Billy remembered Judson very clearly, and was always plaguing me about when he would be coming home.

Clarice and I sat up all night plotting how I would get my five dollars back from Lester without encouraging him. We agreed it was impossible without my seeing him once more, and figured the best way would be for me to make a date with him, stay with him until I got my hands on the money, and then run like hell. Clarice would be on the door buzzer upstairs and the moment I rang she would let me in, then I'd slam the door in his face.

Since I had stopped seeing Lester, to spite me he had been paying attention to Eva, the plain, prim aide who worked in TB. Before that, Eva and I had been friends, but when Lester started taking her out, she wouldn't have anything more to do with me. The day I told him I would see him again, he broke a date with Eva, and then she really did hate me.

I got home a few minutes early, freshened up, and Clarice and I were watching out of my window when Lester drove up outside the apartment. You could see, even from where we were, that he was looking pretty smug and proud of himself. I guess he figured he had won me back for keeps.

"Now you stay right here," I told Clarice. "I'm not going to let him come in, because we might have trouble getting him out. I'll go have coffee with him somewhere—it shouldn't take over a half hour. Then I'll act as though I'm going to invite him in. But when we get to the door, I'll be in front of him, and when I ring, you press the release—but only long enough for me to get the door open."

When Lester rang my bell downstairs, I went down to the door to meet him, and came outside. He looked disappointed that I obviously was not going to invite him in.

"Let's go get that coffee, Lester," I told him. "I could really use it right now. I'm tired."

"Okay, baby," he led me back to the car and we drove to a little restaurant close by. While we had our coffee I gave Lester a sad song about how broke I was and Billy was needing some new shoes, and when I had him all softened up, I asked if he'd mind giving me my five dollars back.

"Why, sure, baby, sure," Lester said. "I would have

given it to you before now, but you been making it hard for me to see you—"

He peeled off five ones and I grabbed them, giving him a nice big, phony smile. "Oh, thank you, Lester! Come on, let's go home now."

When we parked in front of the apartment I glanced up and saw that Clarice was at her position at the window. While Lester was locking the car, I went up and rang my bell. The moment Clarice pushed the buzzer that released the lock, I slipped inside and slammed the door shut behind me. Lester heard the noise, looked surprised, and followed me to the door, and pulled on it. It was locked tight. I waved at him through the glass, and started up the stairs.

Lester started swearing. I could hear it through the closed door. I looked back. He was standing there, waving his arms and yelling. It was really comical.

When I got upstairs, he was still out front, yelling and threatening me. Thirty minutes later he was still there. It was like he'd gone berserk. He was making so much racket, I began to feel uneasy. As long as he was out there, I was afraid to leave the building.

"Why don't you call the police?" Clarice asked.

I had already had that thought and turned it down. Lester hadn't done anything bad to me, and I didn't want to be responsible for his being beaten. We had mostly white cops in our neighborhood and they were a bunch of bastards. But the worst bastards in the local precinct were a pair of Negro cops who were often sent out on black domestic quarrels. The only

182

Negroes on the local force, these two boys made out with their white colleagues by beating up Negroes worse than the white cops did. We called them the "Hurt Brothers." Because they hurt everyone they touched. I had seen some of the results of their handiwork turn up in ER and it was brutal. I might think Lester was a no-good and a liar, but I couldn't sic such cops on him, and get him beat up just because he was screaming at me.

An hour and a half went by and Lester must have run out of wind, or simmered down, because finally he got in his car and drove away.

He was so angry he didn't come near me again at the hospital. And first thing I knew the word went around that he and Eva had eloped. She was such a plain little thing that I knew he did it for spite. They both came back to their jobs after the marriage, but according to the grapevine, they did not get along very well. They fought all the time and Eva became so upset by all the tension that she started threatening to kill herself.

I was glad to be out of the whole thing—Lester, Ollie, the boys in the basement. Rackets were not my bag at all. And as the time approached for Judson to join us, I found myself as eager as Billy and Martin were to see him. We had been a family once—for a short while. I was hopeful we could be again.

Judson was just as handsome as I remembered him —maybe even a little more so with the added maturity the service and the years had given him. But it didn't take me more than a few days after he came home to us to find out that I wasn't the only woman who thought so. Vain as he was, he just had to have a string of girls to feed his ego. By the time I caught on to the first affair he could laugh about it because he was already off on another.

But by then I was pregnant. And I realized that it was going to take extra work on my part to support us all. Judson had finished high school—a fact he held over me—and he had also taken some college credits while he was in service. He was not a stupid man, either. But he had no ambition. When he first came North he picked up a job, worked a week or so, then quit. When I gave hm the facts of life about the money we needed to live on, he went out and got another job. But he didn't really care about supporting his family. The only thing he showed any interest in was singing. He had a nice enough voice and with his looks he had hoped for a career in show business. But he didn't have enough drive to stick with that either. Give him a drink and something to laugh about, and he was happy to sit back and let the world drift by.

It bugged me as I looked ahead to the extra expenses with the baby that Judson could be so indifferent to his responsibility. The fact that he had enjoyed far more education than I, and yet made no effort to put it to use was almost more than I could tolerate. But when I rode him about it, I only hurt myself. Because Judson had the perfect weapon against me: whenever I nagged him, he went out to one of his girls.

184

I never figured out whether it was because he had served a hitch in the army, or whether it was just his natural vanity, but Judson was the kind of fellow who figured the world owed him a living. While I was pregnant he needed a good excuse to quit working so he developed acute arthritis. His wrists were swollen and he managed to get on veterans' welfare. He used that arthritis bit for a whole year. But five months of welfare money was all I could stand, and I told him to tell them he didn't need it any longer, and to go back to work. He did find a part-time job (I guess to shut me up) but he didn't report to the welfare office that he was working, so by the time they found out about it, he owed them a hundred and twenty dollars. I had never been on welfare before and I couldn't wait to get off. The investigators were insulting. They'd drop in any time and ask any sort of questions. One of them arrived one day when I was home sewing and I was keeping Clarice's kids for her while she shopped. The investigator asked how many of those children were mine. He was sure I was getting extra money for keeping them. I was furious but when I told Judson about it he laughed. He didn't have any pride about taking money wherever he could get it.

With the new baby on the way, and no guarantee that Judson was going to contribute anything substantial to the family's support, I decided that I must find a means of increasing my own income.

I had a long talk with Kilpatrick and she advised me to start working for an LPN. It had been years since I was in a school, but I got myself put on days at the hospital and enrolled in night school at the local high school to make up the academic credits I lacked. That, of course, gave Judson even more chance to run and play. When he was in a good mood, he'd stay home and baby-sit the kids for me. When he was feeling mean or mad at me, he'd dress up and go out and I'd have to get Clarice or a neighbor child to watch the boys. Sis had a baby of her own now and she couldn't help me. And once Judson came home, Jim had moved out to an apartment of his own, and ceased playing substitute Daddy to my kids. I always knew I could call on him if I was in real trouble, but I was ashamed to ask him for the help which my husband should have given me.

Night school, however, proved to be more than I could swing. I couldn't trust Judson to cover for me at home, and trying to keep my full-time hospital job, and cook for the family so there'd be food the evenings I wasn't home, and not knowing whether he'd be there or not, got me down. I found myself missing more and more classes, and wondered if I ever could make it up. I was just about to give up the whole idea of working for an LPN when Kilpatrick sent for me and told me that because of the need for nurses, a new ruling had just been put through that allowed hospital aides to train on the job, with the student nurses, to get their LPN ratings. To qualify for this program, you had to make an application, and, if that was acceptable, take an oral examination. I put in my application at our hospital nursing office, and that

186

same afternoon I was told to report to a Catholic hospital nearby for the oral tests. A nun read off the questions to me. They all related to the simplest of nursing techniques which I had mastered months before. I passed easily, and was then eligible to start in on an on-the-job training program to become a licensed practical nurse.

They put those of us who were working for an LPN with the student nurses. We attended similar classes in pharmacology and medication and were assigned patients for whom we provided total care—except to administer medication. We even wrote the charts. They trained us in every possible procedure, and really made little doctors out of the lot of us. When I moonlighted in private hospitals, I discovered that I had been trained in more procedures than many RNs. A city hospital nurse has to stand on her own so much of the time that she is literally trained to do everything short of pronouncing death. I had watched Kilpatrick function long enough to know how true this was.

My patients were on the east wing of the hospital; and Jennie was working on the west wing. We served as grapevine for each other, passing along the warning when a supervisor or VIP or someone from the city office was on our floor. Jennie also served as my alert when Dr. Durand was making rounds. While we both admired him, it did help to have advance warning of his arrival, so you could finish up whatever job you were doing and get out of his way. He was always a

little scary, and some days he was worse than others.
One morning, I was just finishing giving morning care
to one of my patients, when I saw Jennie at the end
of the corridor giving me the high sign. I walked down
to where she was and she cupped her hand over her
mouth so the RN at the desk wouldn't hear her, and
said, "Meet me in the washroom."

She hurried off one way; I went another, then we
circled and met in the washroom. Jennie was there
ahead of me, leaning against the wall, fanning herself.

"Man, oh man, he's really on the warpath today,"
she greeted me. "Make yourself scarce, Louanne.
Don't even let him *see* you."

"The Red Devil?" I ventured.

"Who else? Just look at that." She held out her
hand which was shaking. But from the Red Devil or
a reefer, I didn't know.

"I was giving an enema to an old bastard who was
putting up a helluva squall, and damned if Red Devil
didn't come in just then and catch us going at each
other. My lord, Louanne, he damned near mopped
up the floor with me! He'll be over on your side any
moment now. So, I'm telling you, stay out of his way."

"What did he do to you?" I asked.

"Bawled me out. Told me if I'd approached the patient the right way he wouldn't have been yelling like
that—" She took a deep drag on her cigarette, and
sighed. "I wish to hell that old boy would get married.
Days like this he drives us all crazy. If he only had a

188

piece now and then, maybe he wouldn't be so mean."

I couldn't help laughing. "How do you know he doesn't? Just because he keeps his nose clean around the hospital doesn't mean he hasn't got a girl—"

"Not him!" Jennie shook her head. "If he had himself a nice lay once in a while he wouldn't be so rough on all of us. But I don't know any woman who has the nerve to smile at him—"

"Haven't you ever seen him with a woman?" I asked. Actually I was curious. Because any man as manly as Dr. Durand was bound to attract women.

"Not that one!" Jennie said sadly. "You'd think one of the pretty nurses would work on him. But they're all scared. You know how the other doctors have coffee with the nurses? I've never seen Durand have coffee with anyone except another staff doctor. Maybe he doesn't like women."

"I bet he does," I said. "He's probably just one of those men who's worked so hard all his life he hasn't taken time to stop and figure what he's missing—"

"I did hear he was married once," Jennie said thoughtfully. "But she died, and he hasn't been seen with a woman since then."

"Well, he may be better off than some of these skirt-chasers," I said. "Remember what happened to Seward?"

Dr. Seward was one of our interns that winter, a young, good-looking fellow, not more than twenty-four or twenty-five years old, and married. But that hadn't deterred him from working up a hot little

189

romance with one of the nurses, who also was married. She had an apartment not far from the hospital, and the story went that they managed to sneak over there each day for a little siesta at lunchtime or in the afternoon before her husband got home. One afternoon they were apparently hard at it, when young Dr. Seward suffered a heart attack, and died, right there in her bed. The nurse's husband was due home in another hour and she was frantic. She put in a call to another intern at the hospital, who was a close friend of Seward's, and told him what had happened. He rushed over to her apartment and between the two of them they got poor Seward back into his clothes and into the friend's car, and then drove back to the hospital. How they got the body out of the car, into the lobby, and into the elevator none of us ever figured out, but the first thing anybody at the hospital knew about Dr. Seward's fatal heart attack was when his (fully clothed) body was found slumped over in the telephone booth on the third floor. Of course a scene like that can't go undetected and before Seward was pronounced dead and delivered to the morgue, the word went around the hospital grapevine, and all of us employees managed to find an excuse to go up to the third floor and file past the telephone booth to view the body.

I did admire the way that the doctor handled the whole thing, however. He certainly had proved himself a real friend, by saving heartache for Seward's widow and possibly divorce for his girl friend.

190

One of the reasons we all speculated so much about Dr. Durand is because sex is so common in the hospital that the fact that he didn't seem to be getting any made him unique. When you've got a small city of men and women locked up together like that, and rubbing against each other all day long, you're bound to have a lot of love affairs going. Doctor-nurse romances were the commonest, since they spent so much time together anyway. But there was also quite a bit of doctor-patient sexual activity. Jennie was working in the women's ward one evening and doing bedcheck when she missed a pretty Puerto Rican girl who had been admitted that same day. Along with her other ailments, her card read 4-plus syphilis. Jennie went out looking for her and finally found her in the little doctors-nurses office being laid by the white intern who had been sent up to examine her.

Jennie didn't lose her cool when she discovered them. She just gave the intern a snotty look and said, "When you have finished with the patient, doctor, would you mind returning her to her bed?"

I was amazed to find we even had sex going on in the crowded, chaotic emergency rooms. During the two weeks I was on duty there, a young West Indian doctor was caught in one of the ER cubicles engaged in oral sex (cunnilingus) with a white woman doctor. They were both fired. It seemed a pity, as much as we needed doctors, that those two couldn't have postponed their fun till they got off the hospital grounds.

191

I continued to work through the fifth month of my pregnancy, and then I went on pregnancy leave from the hospital. I had saved up some vacation time, so that I was able to stay on payroll for another month, and I had managed to save enough money to see me through the birth. When I went into labor, Judson helped me get to the hospital but he didn't stay around for the delivery, which was just as well. Since I had no complications, they didn't give me any kind of anesthesia and I did quite a bit of screaming and hollering. The female staff doctor kept telling me it was a natural birth and they didn't believe in giving anesthesia unless there were complications. But there was nothing natural about it to me. I got good care, but I really would have liked some pain killers and by the time the baby arrived I was mad at him too. Because I was still in the delivery room when the lunch trucks arrived on the floor. The baby was already born, and I was relaxed and starved. If I'd still been in my bed I would have got a full lunch, but I knew that, the way it was, I'd only get broth and jello, and I surely could have eaten a two-pound steak. He was a lovely baby, a big nine-pounder whom we named Judson after his father, and he must have got his appetite from me. As soon as he learned about food, he squawled every three hours on the hour, so loud that the nurses who ran the nursery complained he kept all the other babies awake. I got so self-conscious about all the noise he was making that I took him home on the fourth day, although the doctor had

192

told me to stay five days and they didn't need my bed.

Judson and the two boys loved the baby from the moment they saw him. For once Judson was a real help to me. I started working again when the baby was one month old and we took turns caring for the baby. I didn't even pester Judson about getting a job, because it was such a relief to me to know that when I was working he was caring for the baby.

When the baby was six months old, we were so very short of money I decided to start moonlighting, and work a shift at my hospital and then a second shift in a nursing home. With me working double time, I felt I would need more help with the baby than Judson could give me, so I made an arrangement with my brother Bill's wife Alice to keep him. She stayed home all the time with her own children, and she agreed to keep my baby for me. She was such a sweet person that I had no qualms about farming him out to her until we were better off financially and I could take him back.

We carried the baby over to Alice's with all of his things: his clothes and toys and bottles. She was delighted to have him, as were her children. That afternoon I went to work at the nursing home for the night shift. It was in walking distance of where we lived, and very easy work compared to the city hospital. They were mostly old people who weren't very sick and all I had to do at night was get them fed and tucked in and then be on call if they needed anything. I had found that I could catch some sleep while the patients were sleeping. But the night we took the baby to Alice, I found I just could not sleep—for thinking about my baby. Next morning when I got off duty and went home, I found my two older boys, Billy and Martin, both awake and dressed and waiting for me. They had something they needed to talk to me about.

"Mom," Billy told me, his eyes serious, "we really miss that mean baby."

That broke me up and we held a family discussion then and there over breakfast, and agreed that all four of us wanted our baby back. I got a cab and went and fetched him home. He'd only been at Alice's overnight and she and her kids both cried when I took him away.

"Let me keep him, Louanne," Alice begged. "I haven't anything else to do but care for the children. And we love him. It's a pleasure to have him with us."

"Well, after all, it is my baby," I reminded her. "And we four decided we want him back."

Judson and I then worked out a new schedule which we both stuck to. Once in a while I'd pay someone else to come in for a few hours, to give Judson some time off, but the baby did grow up, cared for by one or the other of us. It was one of the nice times in our lives.

CHAPTER *ELEVEN*

Women's Ward

The usual course of training for a practical nursing rating takes eighteen months. But since we were being trained on the job, the hospital administrators decided that we needed more time than that, and the training program stretched out over an indefinite period, as we were shifted from one ward to another, one set of patients and problems to another.

When my baby was about a year old, I was put on the female ward. In a hospital the size of ours the OB ward, while on the same floor as female ward, is separate. Our patients fell into two categories: the young women who were primarily abortion victims, and a scattering of old women who were tumor cases.

It was while I was working on the women's ward that the hospital got its first washrags. All the aides and LPNs were so elated, you would have thought they had given us money. At that, we did not get a washrag for each patient, and with so many elderly incontinent patients it meant that we were constantly washing out the cloths. Nor did we dare to leave them soaking since we had some elderly patients who might drink the water.

The sanitary napkins which the hospital supplied felt like they were made out of fiberglass. They were so rough and irritating to the flesh that poor as the employees were they seldom used the hospital's supply more than once.

By now the men's ward had a regular barber service. But no one came to tend the women. Many of them, who had been at the hospital for a long time, worked on each other. It was common to see the girls who were ambulatory at the bedsides of the bedridden patients, washing and setting their hair, and giving them manicures. Sometimes I even found them cutting one another's hair.

When I was having my baby at the hospital, I had noticed a floor nurse in the women's wing who caught my eye because of her extraordinary beauty and oddly expressionless face. In her mid-twenties, she was a small girl, with a rather delicate but nicely rounded figure. But the thing that held your attention was her hair. It was a waving, alive mass of brilliant red, which no amount of conscientious pinning and pulling back under her starched cap could hide. She also had the coloring to go with it—wide green, slightly vacant eyes and milky skin. The thing that seemed incongruous with all that lush, sexy coloring, was her manner. She was one of the coolest, most restrained nurses I had seen. She seldom smiled. She never seemed to look directly at you when she spoke. She didn't take time to exchange any of the usual banter that goes on among hospital employees. She was never found flirting with the young doctors, although she was certainly young enough to be eligible for their attention. Like Kilpatrick, she was always busy, and she seemed very competent at her job. Yet, as I watched her serve and tend the patients, I noticed that she seldom spoke to any of them, and seemed to make no effort to develop any friendly feeling. Nor did they try to talk to her. She was an efficient machine but she neither offered nor sought communication with the patients.

I asked the older aides about her, and they told me she had been at the hospital for four years. She was a girl of Polish background, named Irene Malinowski. Since no one could pronounce her name, she was called Miss M. None of the aides could recall any scandal connected with her, nor even a romance— which seemed very odd to me, considering her age and startling beauty.

When I began working on the women's ward I ran across Miss Malinowski frequently and found that my first impression had been correct: she was an unusually efficient and conscientious nurse. In fact I seldom saw her so much as resting with a cup of coffee which seemed almost too much dedication. We all had to sit down once in a while to catch our breath. But not, apparently, Miss M. She was always busy, always on the run, and her ward was one of the best run in the building.

One morning I came up to deliver some medication to an examining room off the women's ward. As I neared the room I heard the most terrible cries—they reminded me of an animal being quartered. Inside the room I found a young Negro woman lying on the examining table, her feet in the stirrups, facing the dirty windows which had been slightly opened to counteract the radiator heat. The door beside her was open onto an alcove where the porter's closet was located; the closet door was open and the mopping truck and broom were standing there. Beyond the alcove was the public corridor. There was no sheet over the woman, and a fetus—of what age I could not determine—was aborting, breech presentation. The tiny feet and part of the legs were visible.

There were several other people in the room, but no one was paying any attention to this woman. There were three other patients on examining tables, two doctors, Miss M., a PN, and an aide. None of them seemed to hear the woman's agonized screams. None of the staff was in sterile clothing.

The fetus was still alive, the little feet were wiggling. I could not understand why they didn't take her into the delivery room and take the fetus, and end the misery for both.

An hour later, I came back by the examining room and the woman was still there in the same position, and still screaming. By now the fetus had aborted up

198

to the hip level. It looked to be about four months.

The next time I went by, after another hour had passed, the woman was gone. I saw Miss M. and went over and asked about the patient.

Miss M. looked at me, her green eyes cool and strangely wary. "We took her to the delivery suite a half hour ago. The doctors took the fetus. It is dead. The mother is alive."

"But why—why did they let her lie that way so long?" I asked.

Miss M. looked me over again, that odd expression in her green eyes. I tried to think what it reminded me of—and then I remembered. It was the same kind of a look a dog gives you when he's bracing himself to get kicked.

"I really wouldn't know," she said abruptly, and turned back to her desk, obviously dismissing me.

I decided I didn't like Miss M. Any normal woman would have been shocked by that scene in the examining room, and even if they couldn't say anything in front of the doctors, they could among themselves. I couldn't see why Miss M. put up that barbed wire between herself and me and refused to discuss the case. I was no threat to her.

I was at my locker, dressing to go to my next job, that afternoon when Jennie came looking for me.

"Louanne, guess who was just hauled into Emergency! Eva! Lester's gone and killed her!"

I grabbed my purse and ran down to ER. But when I asked about Eva, I was told she was critically injured but by no means dead, and that she had just been taken over to the neurosurgical wing. I followed her there.

She was in a coma. As soon as she came out of it they were going to take her into surgery where Dr. Durand was going to operate on her back and foot, which had been broken.

"Does anybody know what happened?" I asked Emma, who had brought Eva over to neurosurgery.

"It was one of the neighbor women that called the ambulance and came in with her. Said they'd been having some powerful argument—everybody in the building could hear them yelling—then next thing they knew she was out of the window, and down in the courtyard. Lester claims she jumped—to scare him. They think he pushed her."

"What do you think?" I asked. I had seen flashes of Lester's temper myself but I honestly did not believe he would kill.

"I don't know," Emma shrugged. "He might have pushed her. On the other hand, she might have jumped. She's not a very stable girl, and I've heard her talk about suicide more than once—"

"Since she's been married to Lester?" I asked.

"Come to think of it, that's right," Emma said. "She's only talked suicide since she married him."

I was still with Emma, waiting for Eva to come out of her coma, when the word came over to us from ER that Lester had just been brought in. I went over to see what had happened to him.

He had been delivered by an ambulance and

200

dumped into one of the examining rooms. When I went in to look at him—I started to cry. His face was so badly beaten that if I hadn't known him I never would have recognized him. The eyes were puffed and bruised, the lips slit, a cheekbone smashed in. When they cut away his clothes, there were ugly bruises and welts on his chest, shoulders, back and arms.

"Who did it?" I asked the ambulance attendant.

"Cops," he said. "The neighbors called the cops, and after they took her away they came back and worked him over. But good."

Lester was conscious, but both his eyes were swollen shut so he didn't see me, and I didn't say anything to let him know I was there. But I hung around long enough to hear the doctor's report. Besides the facial contusions, he had been beaten so badly that one lung was collapsed. I wondered if it was the handiwork of the Hurt Brothers. It was clear that whoever did the job damn near killed the man.

Lester survived the beating but always bore its scars. With the one lung collapsed he developed double pneumonia, which then went into tuberculosis. He was treated for TB, and eventually released, and was able to work again, although his face and body both bore the scars of the beating.

Dr. Durand operated on Eva, and patched her together so that she eventually walked, although she had one permanently crippled foot. She never went back to Lester. Sis and I loaned her the money she needed to go back South to whatever family she had left down there.

The mystery of whether it was suicide or attempted murder was never solved. The day that Eva was supposed to appear in court to testify against Lester, he brought her a big bunch of flowers, and she refused to testify. He was not sentenced. After he was released from the TB building, he worked again, but not at the hospital. I never saw him after that.

The morning after Eva and Lester arrived as patients at the hospital, I got to work a few minutes ahead of time and decided to take a walk around the court, and fill my lungs with fresh air before I went in with the hospital smells. As I rounded the north side of the main building, I happened to glance up, and there, at the fifth floor level, which was the women's wing, I saw a woman's body in a hospital gown dangling from the window ledge. Stretched out over her, hanging onto her for dear life, was a slight figure in white nurse's uniform, her brilliant red hair glittering in the morning sun. The patient, dangling from the window ledge, was a big, heavy Negro woman who must have weighed 185 or 190 pounds. Miss M. couldn't have weighed over 110. The only reason she hadn't gone over the side with the patient was because two little aides were hanging onto her, anchoring her inside the building. I thought of going to help them, but I was frozen by the fearful feeling that if I moved she'd fall.

The scene must have been going on for some time because I now saw firemen and a policeman come into the court and try to get a ladder up to the dangling woman. It wasn't long enough. Whatever the patient's original intent had been, she obviously had now decided she wanted to live, because she was struggling to get back inside the window. But she was such a big, heavy woman, that each time she got a foot up onto the window ledge, it would slide off again. Then she'd lose her grip with her hand. And Miss M., who was hanging onto her with both arms, was almost pulled over.

Somebody finally commandeered some sturdy male aides who were just arriving for duty and took them up to the fifth floor. Three of them managed to get braced in the window so they could take over from Miss M. and get a good hold on the patient and pull her back inside.

When I got up to the floor, the PN told me the full story. The patient, who was in for gynecological examination, had been in the hospital for two weeks taking tests, and she had become so depressed awaiting the verdict that she decided to kill herself. Miss M., who was alone on the floor, had seen her going for the window, run after her and caught her. Once she was stopped, the patient no longer wanted to die. But she was already over the side. Miss M. had hung onto her for a full five minutes before anyone appeared to help her, and by the time the whole ordeal was over her arms were nearly pulled from their sockets.

I wondered why anyone who seemed as indifferent to other people as Miss M. did would risk her life like that for a patient. It didn't make sense.

The suicidal patient was sent over to the psychiatric building but eventually returned to the women's ward. The psychiatrist who examined her said she was not mentally ill. Two weeks of lying around waiting to hear whether she had cervical cancer or not was just more than she had been able to tolerate, emotionally. As it turned out, she did undergo a hysterectomy but she did not have cancer.

That afternoon we had a check-out on the ward and I was helping the young Negro girl pack up her things to go home, when Miss M. came by

"When you get finished here, Ferris, come to the nursing office." She smiled. Just the thinnest of smiles. "I'm sure we can both use a cup of coffee."

She turned and hurried off, before I could answer.

As she walked down the row of beds, a Puerto Rican woman called out to her, sobbing in Spanish, her hand clawlike in pleading. Miss M. broke stride long enough to give the patient a quick, impersonal glance, apparently sizing up the need. Then, without a word, she walked on. It was true, there was nothing seriously wrong with the patient beyond sheer misery. She knew not one word of English, and since she was unable to communicate her needs or fears with either staff or her fellow patients in speaking range, she just cried all the time, in Spanish.

When I got back from the morgue, Miss M. was, as she had promised, waiting for me.

She closed the door, offered me a cup of coffee, then sat down opposite me. Her small hand pushed back the stiff white cap in an unconsciously appealing gesture, and when she spoke, she began with a slight sigh.

"You think I'm cold, don't you?"

I was surprised, but I saw no point in lying. "Yes, I do."

"Well, I'm not," she said simply. "I feel the same way you do."

She stopped for a minute and I was silent, too, waiting for her to decide to go on.

"There's no reason I should tell you this—except I want you to know—" She paused again, then plunged ahead. "I always wanted to be a nurse—in the worst way. You know, patching up the dolls and all that nonsense—" she laughed ruefully. "I wanted to nurse people—because I cared so much about people." She took a sip of coffee. "Then I went to nursing school. It was a Catholic hospital, and a very good, very strict school. One day the head sister caught me crying over a cancer case. It was a young mother of four children who had terminal cancer, and I just couldn't accept it, I guess. Well, the head sister really bawled me out. She told me if I behaved that way I never could become a nurse. That I had to learn to control my emotions. It made sense, too, the way she told it. If you put your emotions first, it impairs your judgment of a case. You give worse care. You also frighten the other patients. —It's true, you know," Miss M. sighed. "She was right about it. Sometimes it's hard, though. We lose a lot of cases when the doctors experiment on patients. We lose others through indifference, negligence—all those things that upset you if you let them. But you *can't let them!* Understand?" Her voice rose sharply.

"Yeah," I nodded, "if you start showing your feelings, the ward would be chaos—I know that—"

"Thank you," she smiled. And this time it was a real smile. "I had to learn the hard way, you see. That sister put me on probation. I didn't dare ever show emotion again—or she would have kicked me out of school. I worked so hard at it, that, well, after a while it's a habit—" she shrugged, took another long sip of coffee. "I just wanted you to know—" She got up, set her cap in a firm line and marched back to her floor duties.

I still thought she was overdoing it but I could see what she meant. It was her ward. She was at the top. If she started mooning around over some individual patient, then she might lose control of the PNs and aides who were under her—as well as frighten the other patients. We had been told as aides, if we felt close to tears get in the linen room, or the washroom or somewhere out of sight, until we could present a calm face to the world.

Soon after that I was transferred to Pediatrics which is on a different floor and I didn't see Miss M. again for several months. Then, I was running an errand on her floor one day and needed some adhesive tape, and I went to her wing to borrow it. I recognized her by her trim back and pretty hair while I was still several yards away, and I called to her.

She stopped, turned, saw me, and waited for me to catch up.

"I had to bring a patient up to the west wing, and I need some adhesive," I told her. "May I borrow some from you?"

"Adhesive?" she repeated with a puzzled little frown. Her voice sounded vague and far away.

"Yes, adhesive," I repeated, surprised, "tape." I wondered why she seemed so distant.

"Oh yes, I know," she said brightly, and led me to the supply cabinet and took out a big roll of tape. Then she hovered over me while I cut off what I needed.

When I started away, she put her hand on my arm.

"Don't you want more?" she asked.

"No," I said, puzzled. "I took all I need."

"Are you sure?" Instead of going on about her own business, she continued to stand at my side, holding the tape. Suddenly she giggled. "Why don't you take it all, Louanne?" She pointed across the hall to the ward. "Why don't you take the whole ward while you're at it? Wouldn't you like that?"

I sniffed suspiciously, wondering if she was drunk. But I couldn't smell anything. "No, Miss M.," I said lamely, "this is all I want, thank you," and I hurried off down the corridor wondering what was eating her.

I never found out until several weeks later when I was put on penicillin detail as my first duty as an LPN.

The Penicillin Squad had not been my own choice

of nursing service. But the supervisor had picked me for it, since they needed nurses with certain qualifications for that special sort of work.

"This is really a vote of confidence to you, Ferris," she told me when I received the assignment. "You're a conscientious nurse and you have the right personality for this work. It takes a very special person to be able to go up to perfect strangers and win their trust instantly."

I knew what she meant. I had the kind of wide-open well-meaning face that meant they could make me the heavy who walks up to unsuspecting patients and jabs a needle in their tail before they know what's happened.

There was one thing good about the work: it would take me all over the hospital, so I'd be in on all the action instead of stagnating in one ward. One of the things that I had felt was wrong with the city hospital system was that permanent hospital personnel never rotated duties. It was small wonder that some of the older RNs were so stale and indifferent—when you figured they'd been rotting on one duty for twenty or thirty years. Nor did they bother to keep up with modern techniques and trends in medicine as on-their-toes young nurses, working in private hospitals, tried to do. There was no reason to, since they expected to die on their jobs anyhow.

I had been on Penicillin detail for a few days when I was sent to Miss M.'s ward. I hadn't heard anything about her lately but ever since our last meeting she had been on my mind. There had been something so odd about her behavior that day. I would have sworn she was drunk or on pot. Except that I was sure it wasn't true. With her stern, humorless, self-controlled personality, she was absolutely the last person in the world to be tempted by drugs or booze.

When I appeared on Miss M.'s floor, she spotted me from her desk, rushed down the hall to the elevator, and very nearly embraced me, tray, needles and all.

"Oh, where have you been, Louanne?" she said, staring at me, her cheeks flushed with color. "I've missed you!"

I really had no answer to that odd remark, and I was trying to mumble something polite, when she cut me off.

"Who are you going to shoot today?" she demanded, her eyes bright, as though she were planning a party. "Are you going to shoot Miss Williams?"

I pulled out my list. "Yes, I've got a Williams here."

"Oh, good!" Miss M. clapped her hands together like a pleased child. "And Mrs. Johnson—does she get shot, too?"

I glanced again at the list, and found the name. "Yes."

"And old lady Burton—you can't leave her out. You must shoot her!"

I looked at the list again, wondering why on earth Miss M. didn't look at her own sheet. She was charge nurse and would already have had this information. I was anxious to get on with my job and to the next floor.

As I walked into the ward, Miss M. stayed at my

209

elbow, chattering all the while, about the patients, about me. It didn't make any special sense and I didn't bother to answer. Again I wondered about drugs, but I just couldn't believe it of her.

Instead of going on with her own work, she stayed beside me the entire time I was in her ward, moving with me from bed to bed. It made me uneasy but I didn't know what to do about it. Ordinarily, Miss M. was the kind of nurse that you couldn't make stand still for thirty seconds. When I finished the last patient on my list for that ward, and went back to the hall, she was still with me, still chattering. Occasionally she giggled. In the emptiness of the corridor I looked closely at her. Her green eyes were curiously unfocused, and she never seemed to be looking directly at me. She was obviously in some state of agitation because she kept twisting her hands in a tense, purposeless way.

When the elevator arrived, she suddenly looked directly at me, and her lips trembled. "Why don't you stay?" she asked. It was more of a demand than a question. "Why don't you stay here with me, Louanne. You don't need to shoot anyone else." The word shoot seemed to catch her fancy. She repeated it, and then giggled. "Don't you think you've shot enough people for one day?"

"I have to get on," I said lamely. "I'll come back and see you later," I promised. I got on the elevator. She stood there until the door closed in her face, separating us, her cheeks flushed, her underlip quivering. I wondered if it could be some kind of illness, perhaps a strange fever that was affecting her nervous system? Exhaustion? I made a mental note to ask about her before I left the hospital that night.

Two hours later I was giving shots to some new burn cases, when Emma came looking for me. When I finished my patients she pulled me off to one side.

"Have you been to the women's ward this afternoon?"

"Yes," I nodded. "Right after lunch."

"You see Miss M.?"

"Yes," I nodded again, "why?"

"Did she seem strange to you?"

"I—well, I thought maybe she was sick—" I ducked. "What is it?"

"She's sick, all right!" Emma said. "We had a little emergency today right there on her floor. She cracked up—" Emma circled her ear with her finger. "Went to pieces—right there on her own ward in front of everyone—the patients, staff, everybody. Oh, what a sad sight!"

"Where is she?" I asked. "What did they do to her?"

"Psych ward," Emma said laconically. "Guess she was alone up there and pretty soon some of the other nurses and aides heard her screaming and carrying on. They ran to the ward and she was hanging onto one of the patients' bedposts, giving some kind of big lecture to the whole room. Patients were damn near scared to death. We had to tie her up and haul her off—"

"Does anybody know what she was saying?" I asked.

"Something about love—" Emma laughed. "That was a mighty funny way to show it, wasn't it?"

"No," I said, "it wasn't." I went back to my locker, blinking back the tears as I walked. Before I left the hospital that night I called at the Psych ward and asked about Miss M. They said she would be under observation for several days and could see no visitors until she had been examined.

I had never been to the Psych ward before. Psych was a dirty word to most of us hospital employees for several reasons. To begin with, the administrators, at that time, often used "mental hygiene" or the threat of the Psych ward as a disciplinary weapon over the employees. When they wanted to reprimand an employee, they would recommend "mental hygiene," which meant the employee could not draw his pay until he had clearance from a psychiatrist. Since the psychiatrists were always so stacked up, the worker might sit around for three or four days or even a week before he could get his examination. It was an effective punitive measure because it meant no salary for people who barely met expenses from one paycheck to the next.

The closest I had come to such punishment was when I had the ear infection, and had fought with the Irish aide about my lunch. The Italian RN had said she was sending me over to the Psych ward but the supervisor had countermanded her order, since she could tell I was only hungry.

Once I had been able to save a patient from being transferred from the women's ward to the Psych building. She was in the hospital for a stomach ailment but her record showed a history of erratic behavior and she was suspect, which we all had been alerted to, in case she made trouble on the ward. In the treatment of the intestinal disorder, the resident had ordered that a Levin tube be inserted through her nostril to her stomach. The intern decided the Levin tube was too soft and flexible and he had us put it in a bowl of ice water to harden the rubber before he inserted it. I was working a few beds away from this patient, when he suddenly gestured to me and giggled. A mouse had crawled up onto the rim of the bowl and was sipping the ice water. As I looked up he took fright, jumped off the bowl and scampered down the leg of the nightstand and disappeared.

I was still working in the ward when the intern and resident came by to insert the Levin tube. I overheard the patient telling them, gleefully, about the little mouse that had come to get a sip of the ice water. I glanced up in time to see the two doctors exchange a knowing glance, and I decided I better get into the act before it was too late for the old lady.

"Excuse me, doctors," I said politely, "but I would like you to know that the patient didn't dream up that mouse. He was sitting on the bowl, just as she said, drinking the ice water."

The doctors looked startled, then laughed, and went on about their work. The patient was allowed to remain in the general ward until her release.

Another thing that bothered us all about the Psych ward was that if anyone was sent there, they were admitted at once, without examination, then examined later when the doctors had time to see them. This could mean that a person who was not really mentally ill could be thrown into a room of disturbed patients. Aides who had worked there had told me how alert you had to be around those people. Turn your back and one of them might run up and knock a tray out of your hands, bite you in the back, or try to pull out your hair. The nurses and aides who worked there were not specially trained for that duty and there was never enough staff. The only way they could control the patients was to tie them to their beds every night. If a patient was particularly obstreperous they slapped a strait jacket on him. It was some indication of what happens to people who work in such situations that no one who has spent three years in a city Psych ward is allowed to serve on jury duty.

I hated the thought of the delicately beautiful and sensitive Miss M. being tossed in with a roomful of wild ones.

Yet, as it turned out, there was not much choice. She had suffered a nervous breakdown, and was in need of psychiatric care and hospitalization. I guess all those years of suppressed emotion had finally built up into a force that was more than her body and nerves could tolerate.

When I was allowed in to see her, a week later, she did not seem to recognize me. I had brought her a few personal things—cologne and powder, and she played with the bottle and the box all the time I

214

talked to her but didn't seem to know what they were. She babbled constantly—but not to me. She didn't even seem to see me. She was so far out in left field it was impossible for me to get through to her at all. Her face was white and vacant, her beautiful hair loose and matted around her face.

When I got out of there, I went to the nurses' washroom and had myself a good cry.

I didn't know whether I'd go see her again or not. There was something wildly depressing about that place. It was all the evils of the wards taken one step further, so that it much more nearly resembled a prison than a hospital. While we might be short of utensils to eat with in the wards, these people were given none. They were supposed to eat like animals, tearing their food with their fingers. They had no blankets or sheets on their beds; most of them were tied up at night. There was not one thing that smacked of either comfort or humanity to the place. And woe be to any psych patient who suffered a physical emergency, such as a cardiac arrest or pulmonary seizure, because there was no life-saving equipment of any kind in the entire building. I doubted that the staff would even attempt to haul some over from the other buildings if they did have an emergency. Because it would most likely be a futile gesture.

I went back twice to visit Miss M., but since she did not recognize me either time, I stopped going.

She was under psychiatric treatment for three months, and then released as "cured," and she reported back to work. I went up to her floor to welcome her. I could hardly believe what three short months had done to her. She had never been a big girl and now she was thin to the point of emaciation. All the pretty color had faded from her face, so that it looked pinched, pallid—much older than her actual years. Her eyes were dull green as a stagnant pond. And even her marvelous hair had lost its brilliant color and become a dull grayed-red.

She did know me this time. But she was not especially glad to see me. Or anyone else who was aware that her life had gone up in smoke—in plain view of everyone, there in the ward. I don't know when I've felt so sorry for a person.

I tried to talk with her and cheer her up, but it was no use. She was in control of herself again, but she was just a ghost of the girl I had known. I was not surprised, a few weeks later, to hear that she had quit our hospital for good, and gone out to find a job somewhere where no one knew what had happened to her.

CHAPTER *TWELVE*

The Big Scare

During that time when I was working double time and earning my nursing license, Judson and I had one bright moment. I had built up a few days' vacation leave and when the baby was a little over a year old, Sis took him and my two older boys and her own son, Frankie, and went south to visit our relatives and show our children to them. It was the first time Judson and I had had time alone together since he came back. We spent the week together alone at home, just being lazy and taking long walks and doing whatever we felt like doing. I was amazed that my company didn't seem to wear him down. During that week he never left me. Nor did he tease me about his girls or try to hurt me. It was like a honeymoon. We were closer than I thought was possible. All that we had had for each other that had drawn us together in the first place was clearly there.

But the day the kids came home, he seemed restless again, prowling around the house like a bear that's been too long in his cage. Dinner that night was especially noisy. Both the older boys were full of their trip and wanting to talk about it at once. I could hardly get little Judson to eat his supper and I noticed while we were all waiting for him, that his father was getting that tight look in his face, and playing with his silverware.

"Can't you hurry up that kid?" finally he snapped at me. "Where's my dessert?"

"In the icebox," I said. "I'll get it soon's he's finished."

"I want it now. I've been waiting half an hour," he said petulantly.

"You can wait till he's finished," I said.

And then it was on. The air full of hot words, and then silence after the door slammed. I stared after him, a new thought dawning in my head. I hadn't realized he was jealous of the children.

It was as if our good time together was already no more than a dream.

Once I got my LPN rating, I was determined to guard it carefully. If an RN makes a mistake, there's usually someone around to cover for her or protect her. But if an aide or a PN makes an error, it can easily be the end of her nursing career. If the error is serious, the aide or PN is fired, and the black mark goes on her record permanently so that she is never

218

able to work in a city hospital again. One of the PNs that I graduated with was fired—not for a mistake in nursing procedure, but simply because of a fight with an RN—and she is still blackballed for city work.

The trouble with my new rating, I soon found, was that, like the social friends of a doctor who badger him about their ailments at a dinner party, many of my ghetto neighbors figured I now had enough training that they ought to be able to call on me in a medical emergency rather than bother to go to the hospital.

As I walked down the street in my new all-white uniform, white shoes and stockings, I was often called to by neighbors:

"Mrs. Ferris, would you mind stepping in here for a moment—and help me get a bandage on this boy so he'll stop bleeding?"

"Mrs. Ferris, I got some medicine the doctor gave me last year—and I'm coughing the same way. Don't you think it would be okay just to take this—'stead of going back to him?"

"Mrs. Ferris, would you mind listening to the way this baby's breathing? It sounds croupy to me—"

I tried to explain that I had neither the authority nor the knowledge to help, but sometimes I gave in. If it were something simple, like getting a bandage on right, or helping pull a stubborn tooth, I might get involved. Otherwise I tried to make it clear to all of my neighbors that when they were sick they should go to Emergency, not me.

One day I got a call from a woman I knew who didn't even live in my area. But she had a sister who did, a woman I'd never met. "My niece is so sick," the caller told me, "I was wondering if you could just drop by and take a look at her on your way home from work. She's such a sweet girl and a good student and we're worrying about her missing so much school—"

Like a fool, I went. The mother was on the lookout for me and when I appeared at the door she threw it open and dragged me in. "In here," she said. "My daughter's right here." She pulled me through some enormous, heavy, dark drapes into a stifling, cluttered little parlor room where she had set up a makeshift sickbed. The whole place was dark, dirty, rundown— and somehow evil. It reminded me of a jungle, with the dark, musty drapes and crowded, rickety furniture.

She drew me to the bed where the girl lay, and threw back the covers. I gasped involuntarily, and then I stiffened with anger.

"Your sister didn't tell me this was an abortion. I can't help you."

"Well, you can just tell me what to do then," the mother said cunningly. "Don't you think it would be all right if I just pulled it out?"

"The only thing I'll tell you to do is get this child to the hospital where she belongs," I said sharply.

The girl was no more than fifteen years old. She was partially aborted and obviously in great pain.

"How long has she been like this?"

"Three days," the mother told me. "I did take her

to the hospital, when she started to lose the baby, three days ago."

"Why didn't you leave her there?"

"Well," the mother explained, "she was lying on the stretcher, waiting to be examined, when the baby came out of her. I thought, well, it's all over anyhow and if I just take her back home, there won't be any shame. No one will know she had a baby—so I just tucked the little thing in my pocketbook, and brought my daughter back home—"

What the mother had failed to figure on was the placenta. Although the fetus had aborted, the placenta had been retained. It was now partially out of the child's body. The mother and her sister had plotted to get me there obviously in the hope that I would finish delivering it.

"I can't help you," I said. "Besides the fact it's illegal and you shouldn't ask me to do it, I'm not trained to do a thing like that. I'm a nurse, not a doctor. That child belongs in the hospital."

"Well, I'm not going to take her back unless I have to," the mother said callously. "Because if it's known she had a baby she might not get to finish high school. She's a good student and I want her to get through and go on to college and make a life for herself—"

"Life?" I said, incredulous. "She'll be lucky to be alive—"

"Well, if you won't help me," the mother said coldly, "I'll just have to do it myself. Maybe this will help." She stirred some evil-smelling witches' brew in a Mason jar, poured out a half cupful and held it to her daughter's mouth. The girl drank it.

"We'll see how that works—shouldn't take over a few minutes," the mother said calmly. "Come on to the kitchen, I'll give you a cup of tea."

What I needed was a stiff drink. Even more, I needed to get out of this place.

When we reached the kitchen, I said to her, "I'm sorry I can't help you, but I can't. And I haven't time for the tea, thank you." I had my hand on the door knob.

"Well, if you can't, you can't," the mother said in a cool, offhand voice. "But you can do me one little favor on the way out. I don't want to leave my daughter long enough to do it myself—"

"Of course," I said, relieved to be off the hook for what she really wanted from me.

She slipped down the basement stairs like a ferret, ran back carrying a neat little package, done up in tinfoil, and handed it to me.

"Just put that in the garbage for me on your way out."

Suddenly I was suspicious. "What is it?" I asked.

"The baby," she said, closing the door after me.

I found myself standing outside her door, the package in my hand. I was so shocked I hadn't had the presence of mind to push it back at her.

I stared at it, stunned. It was a human body. Anybody caught disposing of a human body is a criminal.

There was a private hospital across the street. I

started over, thinking I would stick it in one of their trash pails. But as I headed across the street, I saw a policeman saunter past the hospital gate, swinging his nightstick. I swerved, and went back over to the other side.

Before I knew what I was doing I found myself standing in front of my own apartment building. I stuck the package in one of our garbage pails.

Then I went upstairs and started praying. That night I could not sleep. Early the next morning when I heard the garbage trucks grinding on the street below, I ran to the window and watched. The garbage truck stopped in front of our building. Then, to my horror, the garbagemen went to the building *across the street* from us, picked up that garbage, and drove on.

I went to work as usual but I was a nervous wreck all day. Every time I heard footsteps behind me I imagined it was the police come to take me to jail.

I spent a second sleepless night. The next morning when I heard the garbage truck coming again, I got up and ran to the window and watched. They stopped in the street below. The men picked up our garbage, tossed it in the truck and drove on.

I got down on my knees at the window and prayed. "Dear Lord," I promised, "if you let me off free this time, I'll never put myself in such a spot again. Never! I promise!"

A few months after that a young married woman who was a friend of mine got mad at her husband

and decided to do away with the baby she was carrying. She knew a little something about human anatomy, I guess, because she went to a drug store, bought a catheter, and inserted it. She hit home, but when the bleeding began, there was so much of it she got panicky and called me.

"You got to come over and help me, Louanne," she said.

"Like hell I will," I told her. "You get yourself over to the hospital. I don't even want you telling me about this over the telephone—you hear?" I hung up.

I guess she thought I was pretty mean. But I had had the big scare of my life, and I never intended to let myself in for such a fright again.

The hardest case for me to refuse help was also abortion, and it involved a lovely youngster whom I was very fond of, who had just got started on a promising singing career with a group. When she turned up pregnant her mother tried to abort her, but botched it up. She called me at four o'clock in the morning, hysterical with fear. "I think my daughter's dying," she sobbed. "She's bleeding to death."

I loved that girl, and I had to steel myself to do it, but all I said was, "Take her to the hospital at once."

It hurt me to refuse her. If I had not had my license I would have been there at once. I lay awake the rest of the night, worrying about the girl. Sure enough, she was gravely ill, and though she did survive, she was forced to give up her singing career.

What I had been taught about nursing did, of course, make me more alert to the needs of my own children. One morning as I was getting ready to leave the house, Billy told me he didn't feel like going to school that day.

Since Billy loved school and never wanted to stay home even when he was sick, I was worried. "What's wrong?" I asked him. "Where do you hurt?"

"My throat hurts."

I examined his throat, saw that it was inflamed, and got out some of my usual home remedies to ease a sore throat, and left them with instructions for his father to care for him. Often Billy and Martin's sore throats were no more than a prelude to winter colds and I didn't think too much about it. I just knew that it must have hurt the boy quite a bit or else he wouldn't have dreamed of missing school.

Next day Billy's throat was still raw and swollen. By the third day it showed no improvement. I thought he might have tonsilitis. I asked Judson to take him to an eye-ear-nose-and-throat specialist.

When I got home that night, Judson gave me a frustrating report. "The doctor says it's not tonsilitis— but he doesn't know what it is."

I left for work early the following Saturday, while the children were still sleeping. Midmorning, Judson called me at the hospital and told me that when Billy woke up he found that his feet were swollen.

I didn't like the sound of that, but I was reluctant to bring him to the hospital.

"Keep him in bed and I'll get another doctor to see him," I said.

"You ought to put him in the hospital now," Judson said. He was actually right, but we fought about it. I guess I was reluctant to face what I feared was true.

I called a doctor whom I had known at the hospital who was now in private practice in the area, and he agreed to make a Sunday morning house call. I was home when he arrived, and as he opened his bag of equipment preparatory to examining Billy, I stared in amazement. The city hospitals use a special kind of blue alcohol which I had not seen anywhere else. The alcohol that this doctor carried was blue. His syringes had Department of Hospitals written on them. The surgical scissors, needles, were marked CS for Central Supply.

"Where did you get that?" I said, pointing to the surgical scissors.

"Where do you think?" he laughed. "Doctors have to get started in practice some way. I can't go out and buy all this stuff."

I don't know why it always surprised me to find that doctors steal. Actually it was quite common. While I was on penicillin duty, they'd come and ask me for ten or twenty bottles of penicillin and since it was a doctor asking, I'd give it to them—although if I had been caught taking one bottle for personal use I would have been fired. A theft that had really shocked me happened when I first started my course for practical nursing. Since I had to carry scissors and tape in the pockets to my uniform, I left my handbag, with the wallet inside it, in the closet in back

226

of the nurses' station, across from the doctors' cabinets. On that particular morning we had such a high census that all the employees were kept on the run, dragging beds and changing patients to make room for the admissions. When lunchtime came I ran and grabbed my pocketbook to comb my hair and fix up for lunch, and when I looked inside it, every penny had been stolen. I asked the other girls about it. Everyone had been busy on the floor. Then I asked the nurse. "No one was on the station except the doctors," she told me.

"But the doctors wouldn't have stolen my money!" I said.

She smiled at me. "Let me tell you something, Ferris. Doctors are human like anyone else. I've told you never to leave your money any place but in your pocket. The doctors will take anything around here that isn't nailed down—fountain pens, scissors, anything."

Part of the doctors' tendency to steal what they wanted or needed is, I suppose, due to the fact that the hospital uses its interns as a cheap labor force. They are run to death and get very little money. Perhaps if they got better wages they wouldn't have to starve, like little Dr. Porto, or steal, like the fellow who got my thirty dollars, or the doctor who set up practice with hospital supplies. I heard recently that this doctor has such a good practice now he doesn't even bother to take sponges.

After the doctor had examined Billy, he called me

into the kitchen to talk. "It looks like a kidney infection," he told me. "But I can't do much for you. He needs to be in the hospital where they can run tests and determine just what it is."

"I don't want to put him in the hospital," I said. I knew it wasn't rational, but I hated to stick Billy in there, away from school and everything he enjoyed. It was like putting him in prison.

"I'm surprised at you," the doctor chided me. "You know better than that. He needs more care than you can give him here."

"All right," I said. "I won't stand in the way."

Judson took Billy to the hospital. I don't know what it was—but I just couldn't do it. I had the feeling if I took him there, he'd never get out.

Billy did get out—now and then. But never for very long. When the tests were run, the diagnosis was nephritis—a slowly failing kidney function which is not reversible. I started reading everything I could about the disease—to find some hope. There didn't seem to be any.

Judson and I disagreed on every aspect of Billy's illness. Instead of bringing us closer together, like stories would have you believe, it was the wedge that drove us utterly apart. I suppose it was because I knew how seriously ill the child was that I just wanted him to be happy while he could. I wanted him to be home, with books and toys and people he enjoyed. I just didn't want to wish hospital life on him. I knew it too well.

Besides thinking the child belonged in the hospital (which in truth he did), Judson didn't want to believe how serious the illness was. He didn't want to have it close to him, to look at, see and smell every day. Like many parents, he wanted to leave that to the impersonal professionals.

A few days after Billy was admitted to the Pediatric ward at the hospital, I was home, getting supper for my other two boys. I was really feeling sorry for myself that day. Judson and I had been quarreling so much over Billy's illness that he had finally picked up his hat and gone out on the town. I didn't even know where he was. When the telephone rang, I wondered if it was him. Sometimes he called home just to say something mean he'd overlooked when we were fighting.

It was a strange man's voice.

"Your nephew has been hurt. Come to your sister's at once."

I called in a neighbor's daughter to finish feeding the boys and I grabbed my coat and ran out. Sis had given her son a bicycle for Christmas and I was sure he must have run into the back of a car with it, and broke a leg or something. I thought I'd take a bus and then decided not to, because I was afraid I was going to cry. My brother Bill lived a few blocks from my place, on the way to Sis's, so I stopped by there. My sister-in-law Alice gave me coffee and suggested I call over and see how things were. When I called Sis's number there was no answer. I stayed with Alice and kept calling, since there was no point my going to Sis's apartment if no one was there. Finally, after about twenty minutes, Sis answered.

"How is Frankie? Is he all right?"

There was a long pause. Then she said, "He doesn't live here any more."

"What are you talking about?" I asked.

"He doesn't live here any more. He's gone."

"Gone? What do you mean? Did you take him some-place?"

"No, Sis. He's gone forever. He's dead." She hung up.

When Alice and I got there, we found Sis sitting in a chair, staring into space. She wasn't crying. She never did cry. She was like a zombie—past any communication. Her husband couldn't talk to her. Neither could any of us. She was not a drinking woman but she had a water glass full of whiskey in her hand.

She was like that for five days. No one could console her. She would not let Frankie's things be touched. When her husband took away his sled, she made him bring it back and put it in the closet. When he threw away the boy's toothbrush she dug it out of the garbage and put it back in its place by the washbasin. She wouldn't even let anyone throw out the remains of a cake she baked for him, or the bowl of red jello in the refrigerator.

The man who had called me was a passer-by who had found the child's body in the street. Frankie had been playing on the front steps of Sis's apartment building, when the super told him to get off the stoop

230

and go play in the park across the street. As he crossed the street, he was hit by a truck. No one saw the driver. He gunned the engine, and barreled on. When we talked to the police they brushed us off rudely. They didn't even bother to investigate. The owner of the corner drug store told me he thought the driver was a white man.

That was all I needed.

I went to work the same night that my nephew was killed. I was so full of rage at every man—especially every white man—that I wanted to take out my revenge on all the patients that I touched that night. I was just itching to give my first injection. We were using aqueous penicillin in those days and it burned like hell, even under the most careful conditions. I couldn't wait to shoot a patient—and blow him sky high.

I got out my cards for the night, selected an all-white male ward, and got my syringe ready and headed for the first room. If that syringe had been a gun I would have killed the first man I saw. I marched into the ward where the men lay sleeping, snapped the bright light on overhead, went to the first bed, grabbed the covers and yanked them off, in order to wake the sleeping patient as roughly as possible.

The old man blinked, looked up, then smiled, his pasty white face lightened with pleasure. "Why, it's Mrs. Ferris!" he said happily. "I'm always glad to see you, Mrs. Ferris—even though that needle sure does hurt!"

I just stood there a moment, my hand frozen in

midair. He was no one I really knew. Just another old sick man that I had tended now and then. He looked like a skinny old rooster lying in the bed, his sickly white body picked clean of flesh, his face little more than the bones that held it together.

The muscles of the naked hip exposed to me had long since lost their tone, and lay as limp against the bedsheet as the lifeless body of a dead child.

Sick, sad old man, what did he have to do with it? He was a victim, too, just as surely as my little nephew had been. A victim of someone's neglect, some other human being's indifference. How could I hate him?

I leaned over and rolled him gently onto his side.

"It'll only take a minute, Dad. I'll try not to hurt you."

CHAPTER *THIRTEEN*

Can We Be
a Family?

Sis didn't let anyone console her about her son's death. She didn't want to talk it out to anyone; she didn't want anyone's sympathy. She just kept it all bottled up inside of her, and insisted on grieving alone. I tried to get through to her —first with sympathy, then finally I got sick of her. "You weren't the only one who loved that child," I reminded her. I took her my Bible but she wouldn't look at it. "If there was anything in it for me," she said, "I would still have my son."

Gradually she did get over it, of course, at least to the point that she could work again. But it was as if she had buried her heart with that boy. She didn't have anything to share with anyone any more. Her husband was a good, responsible man. And this was the time she should have needed him most. But she wouldn't share her grief and he couldn't cope with her. Finally he gave up trying and they separated. From that time on whatever feeling she had for other human beings went into her nursing. She never had a husband or child again.

Despite my fears about putting Billy in the hospital, he was not actually unhappy there. Maybe it's because most women have a soft spot in their hearts for children, but our finest nurses were in pediatrics. It was also the scene of a quiet, unheralded kind of integration. Most of the children were black; most of the nurses were white. Yet the nurses often became so attached to the children that it was common procedure for them on their own to get permission to take a child home with them weekends or holidays, children that either had no family, or whose families were indifferent to them. I never went to the ward without witnessing some evidence of love between nurses and their small patients.

Billy was such a likable kid, anyhow, that it wasn't long before he was being spoiled with attention. He loved to draw and we kept him supplied with sketch pads and pencils, and he often amused himself—and all of us around him—making caricatures of the staff and the other children. One day when I slipped in to visit him on a very busy day during my own lunch hour, he made a sketch of me—with an untidy, unflattering hank of hair sticking out from under my cap. "Why did you have to put that in the picture?"

I complained. "You don't understand art, Mommie," he told me seriously. "An artist has got to draw it like he sees it!"

Billy was also a great reader, and loved to hold long conversations on any subject with any adult who would take the time to talk to him. Even the rushed young doctors became attached to him. One pediatric intern stopped me in the hall one day, to ask, "Where did you get that child? He's the most intelligent child I've seen."

Today nephritis can be arrested, but in those days it was irreversible. There was nothing to do for Billy except see that he had good care and was comfortable as possible, while we waited for him to die.

We brought him home for a while. But he was already a very sick child. He couldn't go to school; he couldn't even go out of the house for walks. He did have the TV and his parakeet and his fish to play with, and he made his own puppets, and put on shows for us in the evening. I would like to have kept him home longer, but his condition constantly worsened and he needed more care than his father was prepared to give him. Judson wasn't working. But even though he could see it with his own eyes, he didn't seem to understand how gravely ill Billy was. The boy was on a restricted diet and it was vital that he be fed on time. Yet Judson would not even bother to come downstairs at lunchtime if he felt like staying in bed. I had a neighbor who watched and checked for me and if the boy had not got his lunch on time, she went over and fixed it for him. Nights when I'd come home and Billy told me she'd had to come that noon, I'd go to bed and cry my eyes out. How could that bastard just sit there and not bother to get off his behind to fix the child's food! One night when I came home Billy himself was in tears and he said he'd rather go over to my neighbor's house to stay while I was gone. Then I knew it was time to put him back into the hospital.

Judson didn't like the idea. "Why should you stick him back there? He's happier here with his own things in his own house."

"He's got to have good care," I told him. "He's getting weaker all the time. He needs constant attention."

"He'll get over this," Judson insisted. "He's going to get well. Leave him alone!" Judson was very excited, and obviously frightened. He simply could not accept the fact that there was no hope.

"Billy can't get better," I said. "Don't you understand? Will you take him or shall I?"

"You're wrong!" Judson shouted. "No, I won't take him back there. There's no need."

In the end I had my brother Jim come over and pick up Billy and take him back to the hospital. I would rather have kept him home longer, but I couldn't do it unless I was there to nurse him. And I couldn't nurse him at home and make a living too.

When we carried Billy back to the hospital the second time there was a new RN on the pediatric ward. She was a young Jewish nurse, not long out of training, with lively light-flecked blue eyes and soft brown hair. Her skin—which had a natural glow to it —made her seem beautiful, although feature by feature she was not that unusual looking. I liked her the moment I saw her. There was something so open about her, about the way she talked, and the way she worked. She was a different kind of nurse from any I had known before.

Billy liked her too. When she found a bed for him and got him settled, she talked to both of us, in an easy, friendly way. There was nothing syrupy about her, like some women put on when they talk to kids. Just friendly and forthright.

"You never were in training here, were you?" I asked her.

"No, I trained at—" and she mentioned the leading university medical center in the city. She had, since graduation, worked at several voluntary hospitals, and she was only temporarily working for the city on a per diem basis for experience. As I listened to her talk with such enthusiasm about her work, I realized what a pleasure it was to find a nurse who was so fresh and modern in her approach to her job.

I went to see Billy each morning when I arrived at the hospital, before I went on duty, and every afternoon before I went home. I was with him the next morning before going on my shift when Dr. Durand appeared in the children's ward to check a little girl on whom he had performed hip surgery. When I saw his big shadow loom in the doorway I automatically came to attention and stopped talking. But for once the ward did not grow silent at his appearance. Besides the small restive sounds made by the children, there was a clatter going on in one corner of the room. I looked over and saw that it was the pretty new nurse, Miss Lorne, who was going about her business oblivious of our VIP visitor. I tried to give her a high sign but she was not looking my way. She was, in fact, making a great deal of noise fitting an oxygen tank onto the base of a hospital utility cart.

I saw Dr. Durand's big lion head go up as though he sniffed trouble. He glared at the corner of the room where Miss Lorne was working, then stalked over to investigate. Busy with what she was doing, she still had not noticed him until he strode down to her. I held my breath in anticipation. Poor girl—someone should have warned her.

"What the hell are you doing?" He had stopped directly beside her, and was staring with obvious disapproval at the cart.

Miss Lorne did not jump at the sound of his voice. She looked up, saw that it was someone worthy of her attention, straightened up slowly, pushing back a lock of soft hair which had shaken free from under her cap. "I'm setting up an emergency cart, doctor."

"On whose orders?"

"No one's," she said smartly. "It's my own idea." She pointed down the long corridor where the lifesaving equipment was scattered willy-nilly along the walls. "It's ridiculous to have this equipment where it is not readily accessible. If you can't get it to a patient in four or five minutes you might just as well forget it, anyway. Either they are dead—or brain damaged from lack of oxygen."

Dr. Durand crossed his long arms over his chest and tilted back on his heels. "Now, who told you all that?" he baited her. But I noticed his voice had dropped a notch. He looked as though he was beginning to enjoy the exchange.

Miss Lorne held her ground. "I was trained in emergency team work," she explained. "We had an RN, PN and aide working together. And all our emergency equipment was kept together where it was immediately accessible. We were able to save a lot of patients—especially the cardiac arrests—because we could move so quickly."

"You're not a city nurse then?"

"No," she said. "I'm working per diem here."

"Why?" he asked.

"First of all, the city's crying for nurses. But, more than that, I wanted the experience." She dared to smile at him—directly into his face. I would have given anything to see his reaction, but his back was to me. "I've always heard that a nurse doesn't know what patient gratitude is unless she's worked in a city hospital. Most private patients think care is something they can buy."

Dr. Durand semed to be studying her face for a long moment, but he had nothing to say. Then, abruptly, he turned and went back to his patient and began his examination. Miss Lorne went back to assembling her emergency cart.

I couldn't wait till I got downstairs to tell Jennie. "He did it!" I hissed at her as we passed in the hall. A few minutes later in the washroom, I gave her the whole scene. When Jennie heard that the Red Devil had actually been observed in conversation with a girl —and a pretty one at that, she nearly fainted. "I don't believe it, Louanne. You made it up," she accused me. "Life isn't that good to me!"

"He was in no hurry to quit talking to her, either," I reported. "I think if he hadn't forgotten how to talk to people he might have kept on going—"

"You keep watch now, you hear?" Jennie said. "I want to know everything that happens." She smiled broadly in contemplation. "If you catch them together for more than five minutes, I'll buy you a drink to celebrate!"

"Now don't get your hopes up," I cautioned her. "Saying two or three sentences to a girl and marrying her are two different things—"

"Yeah," Jennie admitted. "But this is the first time we've even had a prayer—"

I continued my assignment on the Penicillin detail because there were actually few nurses who did this particular job well. It was ticklish for a number of reasons. An obvious one was psychological. I experienced little trouble with the patients except for one old Italian man who expressed his opinion of the procedure by spitting right in my face. If we'd been on the

240

street I would have smashed him one, but I had long since learned to leash my temper with sick people—they simply are not fair foes. Another bugaboo of the penicillin work was the constant danger of infection from a dirty needle. I was very conscientious about the sterility of my equipment, but I noticed that some of the other nurses were not so careful. There was one elderly Englishwoman on penicillin detail who always carried her own little kit which she made up herself instead of taking sterile equipment fresh from supply. One day when we were on duty together, an aide that we both knew, a tall, handsome mulatto girl, came to us and said she was feeling sick and thought she had a throat infection and would one of us give her a shot? The English nurse said, "I'll fix you up," and got out her kit and gave her the injection.

The next day I heard that the mulatto aide had become feverish and had been put to bed in the female ward. The following day was my day off for the week and I was at home, resting, when I got a call to report to the hospital at once.

The superintendent took me to the female ward where the aide was now a patient.

"This girl has hepatitis. Did you give her an injection of penicillin?"

"No," I answered truthfully. "I did not."

"You must have," the superintendent said. She turned to the patient. "She gave it to you, didn't she?"

The aide looked at me and looked away. "If you say so, then she must have."

I couldn't believe my ears. "I did not give you an injection," I said hotly. "You know damn well I didn't."

"Well, if you didn't give it to her, then you must know who did," the superintendent said.

"Yes, I know," I admitted. "But I'm not going to say."

"You better tell me who it was, or you will be charged," the superintendent threatened.

I looked at her. She was a tough woman, but she had been fair to me in the past. I decided to argue my case. "In the months that I have been on this service I have never had a patient of mine get hepatitis from a dirty needle. Don't you agree it's odd that I'd get one now?"

"Yes," the superintendent said thoughtfully. "I don't think you did it, Ferris. I'm not going to bring charges."

I knew what really made up her mind for her. They were very short staffed at this time and they had to have a nurse they could trust doing penicillin work.

The aide recovered, and a month later she sought me out and confessed what really had happened. She was a married woman with a nice husband and two children, but she had a lover and she had got pregnant by him, and had a secret abortion which she didn't want her husband—or the hospital—to know about. When she felt feverish she feared infection, but didn't want a doctor to examine her for fear she would lose her job, so she had asked us for penicillin.

"—and then let me take the rap," I said bitterly.

"I couldn't tell the truth," she said. "I'm sorry."

When the other employees heard the real story, they thought I should have paid her back. "Why don't you kill her, Louanne?"

Many of them were genuinely disappointed in me that I did not.

Eight months after Billy's case was diagnosed, the resident told me, "I can't tell you how long he will last, but it's just a matter of time. Do everything you can to make him comfortable. Give him anything he thinks he would like to have—"

Billy didn't like the hospital food so I started making things at home to bring to him that he would eat. He loved cornbread, and I learned to make saltfree cornbread which he could eat with the saltfree butter. When I left the hospital at night I would go home and make bread, fix supper, get four hours' sleep, wrap the bread in foil and take it with me to my second job. When I got back to the hospital the next morning I'd put it on the radiator and get it warm and then take it to him for his lunch. Often it was all he ate, the cornbread and a glass of milk. I also made saltfree mayonnaise, and brought him chicken sandwiches from home, and corn on the cob which had been roasted in the husk.

Those afternoons that he wasn't feeling well I'd go home and then come back before I went to my second job. Judson went to see him once a week, on Sundays. He always went at a time when I couldn't go, so we never visited him together. Even the doctors and nurses and aides noticed that we never came together, like other parents did. Judson wouldn't go with me. He claimed that he spaced his visits so that Billy would have a visitor each day, and he picked the time I couldn't go.

The worst part of the hospital's pediatric care was the lack of night staff. There was a reasonable coverage of the two wards until four o'clock. Then the staff dropped to one RN for the two wards, and one aide to each ward. At five o'clock the RN goes to supper, leaving each of the two aides responsible for serving and feeding from forty to forty-five children.

Unfortunately, at just this point when personnel is most limited, the children are apt to be most keyed up and active. If they haven't felt sick all day, this is the time they get sick. And there is no doctor on pediatrics. If there is an emergency, the aide or RN calls a doctor at the staff house, a distance of five city blocks away. His line may be busy, he may be eating or in the bathroom. By the time he gets the call, and walks over to the building the child may well be past help. After midnight, there is a doctor on call in the building, but he is on call for seven hundred patients.

Children, like the elderly, die quickly and pediatrics is the scene of many accidental deaths. I was visiting Billy one afternoon when I saw a student nurse start to feed a Puerto Rican boy with a Levin tube. She got the tube into the child's stomach—but she did not stop to make certain that it was in the stomach rather than the lung. She filled the syringe with eggnog, and forced it down the tube. As I watched, the little boy's face turned blue. I realized he was dying before our eyes—drowned in the eggnog which was filling his lungs. I called to her, but it was too late. By the time she got the tube out of his lungs he was dead.

Despite the proficiency with which nurses and doctors poke tubes and needles into people, we don't really know what we are hitting unless we test it. I never dared give a penicillin injection without first aspirating, because no matter how many times you do it and how good you think you are about hitting a muscle, one in ten or twenty times when you aspirate you look at the syringe and say, "Hell, there's blood in there" and realize you're in a vein, instead of muscle. I watched one intern stick a needle into a young Negro man's spine to take a spinal tap one day; apparently he pushed the needle in too far and severed the spinal cord because that man never walked again.

We had a lot of deaths in pediatrics from tonsilectomies. A healthy looking child would go up to surgery for what sounds like such a minor operation—and die a few hours later of allergic reaction to anesthesia.

I was sitting beside Billy's bed another afternoon when I glanced at the next bed, where a toddler lay, and, to my horror saw him take his finger out of his mouth and stick it into an open wall plug. He let out a shriek when he received the shock. I was surprised it hadn't killed him. I moved his bed away from the wall and reported the open fixture, but nothing was done about it.

The supper hour in pediatrics was nearly always chaos. For the most able and conscientious aide, it was a next to impossible task to feed and care for the forty to fifty children singlehandedly. Invariably, at least one sick child was vomiting. There was always one screaming for personal attention. Usually one was on the verge of death. There were five or six oxygen tents to be checked. And the telephone rang constantly. The best-intentioned woman in the world could not cover everything. And some aides were indifferent. One evening as I walked into the ward a wall of heat hit me. The radiators were on full blast and not one window was open. The aide on duty that night was one of those heavy, shuffling older women who is always tired and always run to death and who just gets through each day for that chicken leg or pork chop and glass of wine waiting at the end of it. I could tell by the way she was shoving the supper trays under those sick children's chins that she didn't really give a damn about any of them.

I asked her if I could raise a window. She threw me an annoyed look and didn't answer. Since I was only a visitor in the ward I didn't do it without permission. But as I stood in the doorway watching the children, it seemed to me that their little heads were going over like flowers in the heat. I saw Billy's head droop on his neck and he vomited across his dinner tray. When I went to help him, the aide yelled at me, "Leave the room, please!"

I walked back to the door and waited. But she went on passing out more trays, and made no effort to clean

246

up the mess. I stood it about five minutes and then went over to Billy and began to clean up. "If you're not going to do it, then I will," I told her. "I work here too."

She looked surprised, shrugged, then let me do her dirty work for her. Later she followed me to the elevator when I left. "I'm sorry," she said. "I didn't know you worked here."

"And what difference should that make?" I asked her. "What about the mothers of those other kids in there—who don't work here. Should their children get worse treatment?" I was so angry I thought I'd report her. But I couldn't find the superintendent and then I simmered down. The aide wasn't a bad woman. Most of the time she was fairly good with the kids. What upset me was that she didn't really care about them.

The new RN, Miss Lorne, did care. She was very self-contained, very efficient, but she had her eye on each one of those children. Not in a sentimental way, like some nurses, but in the highest professional sense: she gave them the most thoughtful care she knew how. Some days when I went to the floor, if the sun were shining I found she had moved Billy out on the porch so he could enjoy the fresh air for a while. He told me that whenever she could take the time she sat and talked to him, and answered all his medical questions and told him about the hospital where she had trained. I never saw her fondle or fuss over him, but he was crazy about her. He felt she was his friend.

The tragedy of Billy's illness was that as the months dragged by, and the nephritis turned into fatal nephrosis, the uremic poisoning invaded his system so that eventually his brain and vision were affected. He gradually lost some of the facilities and controls he had when he was stronger. It became necessary to use a catheter, and a Levin tube, then restrain his hands and legs so he could not pull either tube out. His speech also became effected, and he often lapsed into baby talk. It was heartbreaking to watch the deterioration. I almost didn't blame Judson for visiting him so seldom. It's more than any parent wants to see.

But Miss Lorne continued to treat Billy as though his brain and vision were functioning as well as ever. She talked to him as one adult to another. One evening she came in the room from her own supper break and found the aide giving him a bottle to pacify him.

"Stop that! Take that bottle away from that child!" Miss Lorne cried. "Don't ever let me see you do that again!"

Startled, the aide put down the bottle. "But he has so much trouble eating now," she explained. "It's easier for him—"

"No! I won't have it," Miss Lorne said. She was quite agitated. "So long as that child can eat at all, you feed him with a fork. When the time comes that he cannot manage the fork, you may feed him with a spoon. But don't you ever give him a bottle, as though he were a baby. He's not a baby. He's a boy. And on the days when he feels better, and realizes what you did to him, he'll never forgive you for it!"

I should have known that Billy could not be fooled about his condition. Toward the last of his illness he

248

was only semirational most of the time, but then there were moments when his mind was clear as ever. I was sitting by his bed one day when he appeared to be more or less comatose, when suddenly he turned on me and looked at me as though he could see my face clearly.

"Mommie," he asked, and his voice was thin and shaky, but not babyish. "Mommie, what's it gonna be with me? Will I ever come home?"

I made myself tell him not to worry, things would be okay. But I was lying and I think he knew it.

He had something more than that on his mind. He seemed to be studying it out, and then finally he said, "Do you think we could live like a happy family?"

It was a knife in the heart to me. My God, I thought, sick as he is, he can still wonder about things like that. "How do you mean, Billy?" I asked him.

His words came in parts, but the thoughts were clear. "I mean a family like my family. You know, Daddy and you and Martin and the baby and me. Could we all go on a picnic?"

"Sure thing," I promised, hoping my voice sounded hearty. "As soon as the weather gets warm and nice."

That night I told my husband what Billy had said, in hopes maybe he'd talk to him about it when he saw him on Sunday. But he didn't see it that way.

"A happy family?" Judson repeated. "It's not going to be any different than it's ever been."

"But can't you pretend?" I begged him. "Can't you even pretend for that kid?" But he wouldn't.

Long after they had done enough tests on Billy to

correctly diagnose his illness, the doctors continued to do tests on him. I was getting off the elevator one afternoon when I heard a scream from the ward—and I knew it was Billy. I rushed inside. There was a student doctor I had never seen working over the boy.

"What are you doing?" I asked him.

"It'll only be a minute more," he told me.

He had a needle in the child's groin and was taking a blood sample. There was no point trying to take the needle away from him. I could see by the syringe he was nearly finished. In a minute the needle was out and Billy had stopped shrieking. But I was furious.

I went straight to the resident. "I'm taking that child home with me—right now," I told him.

He asked me to sit down and tried to calm me. "What upset you?"

"Making a guinea pig out of that kid," I said bitterly. "You told me he's dying—why must you make him suffer? I'd rather take him home and let him die in peace."

"But you can't stay with him and care for him, Mrs. Ferris," the resident said gently. "The tests we've taken haven't hurt him for more than a few minutes. And the point is that it's the only way we will ever be able to find cures for other children. It's true your son's dying. But wouldn't you rather have his death contribute something—perhaps mean another child is saved later because of him?"

I knew he was making sense, but I couldn't stand to see Billy suffer any more than he had to. "I don't want him hurt," I said. "He's suffered enough."

250

I didn't take him home that day. Instead I went to see Dr. Durand. I told him I understood the value of the tests, but I would rather see the child die at home with love and neglect, than to leave him here where any student doctor could walk in and jab another needle in him " for research."

He listened me out, and then nodded. "Don't take him home, Mrs. Ferris. You can't care for him properly and work at the same time. I'll put an order through to leave him alone."

"Thank you, doctor!" I wished there were better words to tell him how relieved and grateful I was. But I knew that with him the best words were the briefest. I left.

That afternoon, Miss Lorne was on duty when I reached the ward. "So you made them call off the dogs," she greeted me. "I'm glad, I don't enjoy seeing them experiment with these children, either."

"Dr. Durand seemed to understand," I said, and glanced at her face to see if she would react.

"Yes," she said softly, more to herself than to me. "Yes, he would. He's got a loud bark, but he's an old softy underneath." She walked away, her pretty hair swinging silkily around her cap. I couldn't wait to report the conversation to Jennie.

"Old softy? Wow!" Jennie repeated happily. "She must be getting to know him!" She frowned. "Wonder where they do it?"

Toward the end of Billy's illness, there were several times when it seemed that death was near, and one of the aides would call me and I'd rush over to the ward. Then Billy would rally and get better for a while.

I had ushered so many patients out of the world by now, it was on my mind that I didn't want to be deprived of having that final moment with my son. Each time I left his side I prayed that he would still be there, alive, when I got back.

Once when Miss Lorne caught me praying, she said gently, "Don't pray too hard, Mrs. Ferris. In the condition he's in now it's selfish of you to want him to live."

I felt chastened. I knew she was right. The only peace left for him was death. I looked down at him. He was pitifully deteriorated, little more than a ghost of the active child he had been. I changed my prayer: "Whichever way you decide, dear God, let it be."

Two weeks from that day he was dead.

I got my wish to be with him at the last. It was in the late afternoon, and I had visited that morning, and again at lunch and there hadn't seemed to be any change in his condition—except that he was in a very affectionate mood and crawled up the bed rails to kiss me. When I finished my shift I went back. As I stepped off the elevator, in front of his ward, I saw an attendant coming down the corridor with an oxygen tent, and I knew it was for Billy. Miss Lorne met me at the door and told me she had called for the tent because he was having trouble breathing.

After they got the tent set up, Miss Lorne opened it and he looked like a little doll sitting in there, chiseled and beautiful. She fed him some soup, and then she gave him some kind of hypo. I wasn't thinking very clearly or I would have recognized what that procedure meant. It's almost routine when a patient is known to be dying to give them a little demoral or morphine to ease the journey.

I went over to the tent to listen. His breathing was very labored. My God, I thought, he's dying. I went to the telephone to call my husband. When I couldn't get any answer I called my neighbor next door. She said she'd tell him.

When I had made the calls I walked back to Billy's bed. They had it elevated as high as possible and I stood at the end of the bed and watched him. He looked up at me for a long moment and then his head slowly settled onto his chest, and he closed his eyes. It was the prettiest death I ever saw. I didn't call anyone. I didn't cry. I just stood there, hanging onto the edge of the bed for a moment. And I told myself not to do anything foolish, not to scream or cry before all these other little children and frighten them. I turned and walked out of the room without making a sound.

When Judson got there I told him Billy was already dead. He walked away from me and sat down by himself on the other side of the hall. I told him that the nurse had asked us to stay until the resident could talk to us.

I knew the doctor wanted our permission for an autopsy. While I hadn't wanted the child subjected to painful experiments while he was alive, I was willing to have his body examined for whatever benefit it could be to the study of the disease.

But when the resident came and asked our permission, Judson said, "No."

I didn't try to argue with him. It didn't seem the time or place.

My brother Jim came to the hospital to pick us up. But Judson cut out on his own. He didn't go home. He stayed away several days. He showed up when his mother arrived for the funeral. Sis and I made all the arrangements and selected the coffin. Judson wouldn't have anything to do with any of it. He even refused to walk into the church with me. It was almost as if he was saying the whole thing wasn't true, that it hadn't really happened.

When the service was over we all went back home and I went into the bedroom and lay down on the bed. My mother-in-law followed me and sat down in a chair beside the bed.

"You always said you didn't want my son."

I couldn't believe she was going to start in on me now. "I never said that," I protested, wishing she'd go away and leave me alone with the tears which had finally come.

"You've acted like it," she said in that flat, accusing voice of hers.

"What do you mean?" I asked. Except for her habit of baiting me, I couldn't think what she was getting at.

"You've managed to make something of yourself—considering where you started from," she said. "You got yourself a life now. You don't need my son any more. Or the boys. Let me take them back South where they'll be happy."

"You want to take my children away from me?" I sat bolt upright on the bed—unable to believe any mortal woman could be that cruel. "When I've just lost my son—you're asking me to take away my other two boys? Are you crazy?"

"They don't get much from you," she said. "You're too busy. You like your work. I don't see why you won't let me have my son's children. I'd give them more attention than you do."

"Do you know why I work so hard?" I spat at her. "To keep bread in their mouth, that's why. I suppose you think I stay away from home because I want to!"

"How would I know?" she shrugged.

"How else do you think they'd eat if I didn't work?" I asked her. "Do you really think that pretty son of yours feeds them? You didn't raise him to turn his hand. You brought him up thinking he was too damn good to work—" This was getting to be dirty pool and I knew it but I couldn't stop. She had cut me and it was all I could do to keep my hands off her. "Go ahead—" I taunted her. "Take back your son. You can have him. But if you touch either one of my children, I'll tear you apart—" By now I was halfway off the bed, my hand raised to strike her.

She was not a hysterical woman. She eyed me with that cold cat's eye of hers and she said, "You're threatening me."

255

"You're damn well right I am," I yelled at her. "This is my house and I want you out of it. The sooner the better—"

"We'll see what my son says about that."

"It doesn't matter what your son says about it. I pay the rent."

She took her time getting up out of my chair, and left the room. The next day she took a bus back South. It was the last time I saw her.

There is a saying that to be a good nurse, a woman should have borne a child, undergone surgery and lost a loved one.

I had yet to have an operation.

256

CHAPTER *FOURTEEN*

Mothers Are
for Emergencies

Judson moved out soon after Billy's funeral.
It was ironic that the problem that I had
pestered him about for so many years was solved by
our separation. As soon as he found himself on his
own, and had to pay his own rent and buy his own
food, Judson began to work steadily and he has worked
ever since. That fact alone was enough to give me a
sober second thought about myself and my marriage.
I realized that I had been too busy working and too
worried about paying the family bills to ever do much
for him. Perhaps if I had taken time to try to help him
figure out what he could do, he might have had a
better chance to make something of his life. Instead,
I had ridden him about his lack of responsibility. And,
to get even, he had done things he knew would hurt
me.

Now that the daily fights were over, we found, to our surprise, that we actually could be friendly and polite with each other. Judson dropped by to see the boys at least once during the week and on Sundays he usually took one or both of them for the full day.

I didn't miss him when he left, simply because we had got to the point where we did nothing but attack each other. But I did miss having a man in the house. Life seemed empty and pointless now that I had lost both my son and my husband. To fill up the void, I turned to my work, convincing myself that I had to work extra hard to take care of my two boys and myself, now that I was alone. In addition to my full-time job at the hospital, I moonlighted a full extra shift at a private hospital four days in the week, which meant that on those days I was working sixteen hours, and had no time for myself, or my sons. When I was home, I slept.

What I couldn't see, at first, was that I was boxing myself into the same sort of position that Sis had taken when she lost her son. Rather than face my own grief and loss, I was crowding my days with duties and routines, to avoid thinking or feeling. Even when Jennie came to me exultantly one day with the big news that we had so long awaited: that Dr. Durand and Miss Lorne had married—I felt nothing. I was glad for them, in a detached kind of way, but I wasn't thrilled as I might once have been.

Then something happened that jolted me out of myself.

My sister-in-law Alice, of whom I was as fond as if she were my blood sister, was told by her doctor that she must undergo a hysterectomy. My brother Bill had a little money ahead and he insisted Alice go into a pretty, private hospital in our area, where she would not have to endure the unpleasantness and possible humiliation of the city hospital. Sis, whose specialty was surgical nursing, tried to dissuade Alice from going there because she felt the city hospital, bad as it is, was a better spot to be in in case of postoperative complications. But Alice's surgeon was affiliated with the private hospital and she preferred to go there. I worked the day of her operation, and when I joined Sis and the family after work in Alice's room at the hospital, she seemed alert and was apparently doing well. Then, suddenly she went into convulsions. She was in shock, we found later, from internal hemorrhaging which had not been discovered because the hospital staff had neglected to check her blood pressure following surgery. Sis and I went into action and called for help. But the next few hours were an absolute nightmare. Alice's surgeon had left the hospital and could not be reached. There was no supply of blood available. They had to take oxygen from another critically ill patient to give to her. And all the while Alice was in such intense pain that she was bouncing around on her bed like a tennis ball, screaming, "I don't want to die!" Yet all Sis and I could do for her was hold her down and beg for help—which came too late. By the time the doctor arrived and took her back up to surgery, she had been in shock over four hours, and she died on the operating table.

All the grief that I had held back since Billy's death spilled out of me now. I wept for days. For her, for Billy, for my marriage, for myself. For all that had gone wrong with my life.

Then, when I finally stopped weeping, tired and limp after the release of those long-bottled-up tears, I found that I could go on. I had my strength back.

I was luckier than the other ghetto working mothers, in that I was able to make enough money to hire a babysitter now and then. Unless they have an old aunt or grandmother to watch their kids for them, most ghetto working mothers are forced to leave their children alone. They may leave the house at the same time in the morning, when the kids are going to school, but school is over at three in the afternoon, and the mothers' jobs are usually in another part of the city, so by the time they finish a full day's work and get home, several hours have gone by since the kids left school.

It breaks your heart to see those kids trailing home from school in the afternoons, some of them no more than six years old, with a house key tied on a dirty string to their necks. With nothing to greet them but an empty house, it's little wonder they get in trouble so young. The teenage girls invite their boy friends to come in with them and next thing you know we've got another pregnant fourteen-year-old. The smaller kids, with no one to supervise them, are subject to attacks

260

from older children and adults. Rape, incest, experimenting with sex and drugs, sniffing glue—your name it, we've got it in the ghetto.

At one point I hired a woman in her sixties to be home when Judson came in from school each day, and stay there till I arrived. I was walking home from the bus stop one night, in the rain, and a few blocks from my house I saw, in the distance, a child playing out in the gutter. He was barefoot, his clothes were soaked through and plastered to his body. He had no hat. His blue jeans had come unrolled and were dragging over his feet into the water in the gutter. I was thinking what a miserable, neglected looking kid that is—and then, as I drew closer, I recognized him. It was my baby, Judson.

He saw me, waved, and ran, tripping over his wet pants, to greet me. "Hi, Momma!" I saw he was perfectly happy, running free out there in the rain. So there was no point bopping him for being wet.

It was the old lady's fault to let him out like that. When I went in to tell her off, I found her in the kitchen, with a pile of empty beer cans around. That was the last time I hired her.

Martin was actually old enough to baby-sit his brother. But the more I asked him to do it, the more he seemed to resent it. And me. He hated to be forced to stay home and watch a kid brother when the other boys his age were out running free on the streets.

I suppose no mother is ever prepared for the moment when she looks into her child's eyes and sees hate for the first time. It's a body blow, a real shocker. You catch your breath, and wonder how it all began. What went wrong between you and this kid you bore and love? As Martin reached his 'teens, I saw that flicker of hate come and go, at the times I asked him to do something he didn't want to do, or the times he obviously felt I was pulling my rank and bullying him. I wondered what I could ever do to to dispel it.

When Martin was about fourteen, he began to rebel openly against me and against his school—and I suddenly realized I didn't have a clue to what was going on in that boy's head. First, it was little things. I'd get a note from his Sunday school teacher that he'd been acting up, and I'd ask him about it and he'd say, "I won't do it again," and then we'd both forget it and he would go ahead and do it again. Then there were notes about pushing on the bus, or running in halls when he was supposed to walk. Nothing big, nothing serious, but it spelled trouble. It came to a head one day when he was supposed to be in a play in the high school assembly. The day of the dress rehearsal he made a terrible scene: screaming and beating on the desk and yelling and acting up so badly that I was called. Before I went to the school, I talked to him and tried to find out why he had behaved that way.

"Oh, I don't know." He obviously didn't want to talk about it but I couldn't go to his teachers without having some idea of what the cause was.

"Come here," I said, and I tried to sound friendly

instead of angry. "Sit down and tell me why you did it. I know you want to be in that play. You love to sing. I was going to go to see you in it. And your father is going to go—now why did you act up?"

"You really want to know?" He gave me a funny questioning kind of look as though trying to read just how much I cared. But he did sit down like I asked him to. "I don't want to be in the play tomorrow, that's why. I figured if I got in trouble today, then I wouldn't have to go tomorrow."

"But why, Martin? When they cast the play, you wanted to be in it. Didn't you?"

"Yeah, Maw, I did," he nodded his head, then he wet his lips as though he was nervous. "But—well, it's like this. When they sing those songs I want to cry about my brother and my cousin. And if I cry the boys will laugh at me and I'll be embarrassed—so I just thought if I made a big scene, they'd kick me out and then I wouldn't have to be there—"

I was shocked, and sobered, to realize how little I knew him. I looked back over the years of his life, and I saw that it had been one kind of tragedy after another—which I'd been too busy to understand. First, when he was so little, there had been several years when he had no father. Then when his father did come home, he didn't use much common sense about the kid. He badgered him, but he didn't help him. If Martin wasn't doing well at school, his father would go there and maybe strike him in front of the class. I found out about that after I noticed that when Judson raised his hand at home, Martin would duck automatically. When his cousin Frankie was killed, Martin didn't want to see him, but a neighbor insisted on taking him to the funeral parlor. I guess he remembered it only too well because when his brother Billy died, Martin wouldn't go near the body. He wouldn't even go to the funeral service—instead he went to a movie that day. And, although some of the relatives complained about it, I let him go because at least I understood that he acted that way because it hurt him too much, not because it hurt him too little. I was thinking all this when I suddenly realized Martin was talking again.

"I don't want them to force me to do it, Maw. Because when they sing I feel like something is in my chest and I can't get it out."

I went to the teacher, and got him excused from singing in the play. After that, I sat down and did some serious thinking. I had our rent and food budget under control. We were not in debt. And I figured out that I could give up my second job and make up the difference by cutting down on food and baby-sitting expenses. Judson was eight years old. I realized that if I kept up the pace I was going, I would know as little about him when he was Martin's age as I now did about Martin.

So I quit my second job. The big thing was I was home much more with my boys, and I was getting enough sleep, too, so that the hours I was home I wasn't exhausted, and I could listen to what they told me. Once, when he was feeling friendly to me, Martin leveled with me about my own role. "After you're a baby," he explained to me, "you only need a mother in emergencies."

That cut me a little and I wasn't sure how to respond. "What do you mean by that?" I asked him.

"It's like this," he told me, his face thoughtful. "If I run in to dress, and can't find a shirt or tie, and yell Momma!, that's an emergency. Or if I come home hungry and go to the refrigerator and don't see what it is you want me to snack on, and yell Momma!, that's an emergency. Or—" and he put himself into a future man's role, "if I was in the air force in a plane that got shot at and I bailed out and said the Lord's Prayer and then the cord still didn't work and I yelled Momma!, that's an emergency."

I noticed how right he was. After the boys reached a certain age, mothers were for emergencies only. They didn't want you to interfere with their friends and their life. And beating a child didn't help one bit. The most a mother could do was advise and suggest in a friendly way. And if she really is friendly, and they trust her, they'll take her advice. Otherwise, forget it.

Although we made a kind of truce, and got along fairly well, I never was able to get close to Martin. When he was old enough to move out of the house, he did so. And he lives rather like his father: works if he has to, but doesn't like working, and shows no particular ambition about anything.

I quit pushing myself in time to be able to get

close to Judson. He was still young enough to be won over and he is still with me: friend, companion, advisor, critic. I will be sad the day I lose him, when he has to go into military service.

One Sunday night when I came home at midnight, I found Martin asleep but little Judson, who had been with his father, was not there. It wasn't like his father to keep him so late. I called Judson's number. There was no answer. I asked another nurse, who lived below me and had also just come off duty, if she would go out with me to look for him. It was a dark, spooky sort of night, and I didn't like going out on the street alone so late. We were both still in our white uniforms and white shoes and stockings and we showed up like twin beacons on the dark street. Just as we reached the corner bar, a man stepped outside, unzipped his trousers, and started to relieve himself, right there on the sidewalk in front of us. We were both shocked, and when we saw a police prowl car going by we hailed it.

The car stopped. There were two cops in it. Beyond the driver who was on the side nearest us, I recognized the good-looking cop who had brought the abortion case into the hospital emergency room.

"That man voided right here in public!" I said sternly to the driver.

By now, the fellow was disappearing back into the bar.

The driver looked puzzled. "He did what, ma'am?"

"Voided. Urinated!" I said.

The other cop whispered in his ear, and light dawned on the driver. "Oh," he said, "you mean pissed!"

"Sorry about that, miss," the other cop grinned at me. They parked the car and the two of them went inside to pick up the exhibitionist.

We circled the block, then went back to my apartment—and found Judson senior waiting for us. He told me he had brought the boy home earlier that night but since I wasn't in, he was afraid to leave him.

I was glad to see that the nice-looking black cop was still in our neighborhood. I didn't think much of the cops on our beat. They were mostly white, at that time, and they were no help at all with our teenagers. We had some bad gangs, and we also had a lot of nice boys. But the cops lumped all the blacks together in their minds without bothering to sort out the good from the bad, and they treated all the boys alike: they were tough on them.

One night there was a party in one of the boy's homes in our block. There were seventeen boys there, ranging in age from eleven to fourteen, including Martin. The party broke up around 11:30. I was working the day shift then, so I had already gone to bed. I heard the sounds of the kids coming out on the street talking and singing and yelling goodnight to each other, and I went to sleep, figuring Martin would be home any minute.

When I woke up in the morning, Martin was not

home. I called some of the other mothers of boys whom I knew had gone to the party. Their sons were also missing. But no one knew where they were. No one had heard anything.

If they were *all* missing, I figured it could be only one thing. I was in a rage as I dialed the precinct number.

Did the cops have our sons?

Yes, they did. They had picked up the whole party of children and taken them all to the station and held them in jail overnight, for "disturbing the peace." They had not notified a single parent. Nor even checked at the house where the boys said they had just come from.

268

CHAPTER *FIFTEEN*

Not All Cops
Are Pigs

I stormed down to the station and demanded my son. "If I wasn't so busy working, I'd sue!" I told the captain bitterly.

"Take it easy, lady, you'll get your kid back."

"And what have you got him here for in the first place?" I demanded. "Because he sang a song in the street? What kind of a free country is this? If your lazy, good-for-nothing cops spent more time helping these kids instead of shining barstools—"

"Watch it, lady—" The captain was getting mad. But I didn't give a damn.

"If I was white and had plenty of money," I told him, "you'd be scared to death that you might get dragged into court for false arrest of minors!"

269

"Come this way, ma'am, I'll get your son for you—" I felt a hand on my elbow, looked around into a familiar face. It was the nice black cop. His face was calm and strong and quiet. But his thumb and forefinger bit into my elbow warningly.

"Let me show you the way—" he said. Although his voice was soft and courteous there was no doubt it was a command.

"All right," I said, suddenly docile. I had shot my mouth. Now all I wanted was to collect Martin and go home.

"Get her kid for her, Stuart, and get her out of here," the captain snapped.

I started to say something sassy, but Patrolman Stuart hustled me out of the captain's hearing before I could think of a smart retort.

"You had your say," he told me, as he led me back to the cell. "Now, calm down."

"Aren't you all ashamed," I demanded, "putting little kids in jail like this?"

"I'm sorry," he said soothingly, in that nice, rich voice of his. "I wasn't on duty last night. Didn't anyone call to tell you they were being held?"

"Not a damn soul. They just rounded them up and locked them in here like a bunch of common criminals. They didn't call a single parent—"

"No wonder you're mad. But we'll have him out in a minute."

We rounded the corner—and faced the cell. I could have wept. It was one big cage, with the usual neigh-

270

borhood collection of winos and dopeheads, sprawled on the floor. The band of boys were all huddled together in the opposite corner, as far as they could get from the adult drunks and junkies. When they saw me coming they called out cheerful greetings. But they all looked scared. And the little one, the eleven-year-old, was crying. Martin automatically stepped up to the door, his eyes bright with relief. "Hi, Maw!"

"That's my boy," I pointed him out to Stuart. "But I don't want just him. I want them all."

"Just a moment, ma'am, I'll have to get permission from the chief." Stuart hurried back to the front desk, returned in a few moments, his eyes glinting with amusement. "The captain is happy to give you the whole crop. I think," he murmured, for my ears alone, "he'll be mighty glad to see you go!"

As he unlocked the cell door and the boys filed out, I couldn't help but think that a good cop like Stuart could get shot one day for what those cruel and thoughtless colleagues of his had done last night. That eleven-year-old would never forget this night. I haven't seen him lately, but he's nineteen now, and I will lay you an even bet he's a cop-hater. And, just like those dumb, chicken-shit cops sized up that bunch of boys, he won't be able to sort out the good from the bad.

"I'll drive you and your son home," Stuart said.

"There are too many of us," I hedged. I was still mad.

"We can walk, Mrs. Ferris," several of the bigger

boys spoke up. "Let him take you and Martin and Jimmy." Jimmy was the eleven-year-old.

"All right." I let the big boys walk home and Jimmy and Martin and I followed Patrolman Stuart to his car. I almost laughed to myself, as he held the door for me. With all the mean things I had thought and said about cops, who would have thought I'd end up taking a ride in a policeman's car?

When we had delivered Jimmy to his door, I directed Stuart to my apartment.

Instead of letting us out, he parked the car, and once again held the door for me.

I hesitated, wondering how to thank him. "I'd ask you up for a cup of coffee, but I'll have to be leaving for work soon—"

"Thanks, I could use the coffee," he smiled. "I'll drive you to work."

The three of us walked silently into the building and up the stairs to my apartment. It was still early in the morning, no more than nine o'clock. The bright morning sun was streaming in the kitchen windows. I put on the coffee pot, then gave Martin some breakfast. Now that the fright was passed, he was exhausted. It was obvious that none of the boys had even tried to sleep that night.

"Come along," I said to him, "as soon as you finish your cereal, I'll put you to bed."

"Aw, Maw—" he started to protest.

"Why don't you do what your mother says, son?" Stuart said softly. "You had a hard night. You need a rest."

Martin looked at Stuart warily. Their glances met, held, as man and boy sized up each other. Neither wavered. Neither smiled.

"Why don't you go on and get some sleep," Stuart urged.

"Okay, I guess I could use it." Martin got up with an exaggerated yawn, and lumbered off to the boys' bedroom. I followed, to help him. He looked tired enough to faint.

When I came back, Stuart had taken off his heavy blue policeman's jacket, laid it neatly over a chair back, and was sitting at the table in his shirtsleeves, thoughtfully sipping coffee. I stood a second at the doorway, watching him. He looked solid and comfortable, as though he had always been part of the room.

"Hi," I said, sitting down opposite him. "You know what? I don't even know your first name."

"Ed," he told me, "Ed Stuart."

"I'm Louanne." Without thinking how silly it seemed, I reached across the table to shake hands. "Louanne Ferris."

He took my hand, held it a moment, then looked sharply at me.

"Husband?"

I shook my head. "Not any more."

"Good." Ed sighed, leaned back comfortably in his chair. "I didn't think so."

"Why not?" I asked, puzzled, and suddenly wary.

"You're too strong, too independent. You look like you can handle things for yourself."

"Mostly I can," I agreed in a low voice. For once I

wasn't proud of it. Instead, I felt slightly embarrassed and somehow inadequate.

"But you don't like to have to," he spelled out my fears for me.

I looked up, and met his smiling eyes, and I smiled back. "That's right," I admitted. "I could use a broad shoulder to lean on now and then."

"What else do you want, Louanne?" he asked, his voice suddenly serious. "Have you ever stopped running long enough to think what you really want?"

"A house," I said dreamily. "A nice, neat, clean little house somewhere. I used to say country, but that's not practical. A house in the city would do. But somewhere better than this—" I gestured toward the center of the ghetto. "Someplace where I can have a porch to sweep, and a place to hang clothes in the fresh air, and maybe flowers in the back yard—"

I had always dreamed of a house for my family— but it was a dream Judson had never shared with me.

"—And a big kitchen to cook in?" Ed prompted me, smiling. "Can you make beans and rice?"

"And the world's best fried chicken and sweet potato pie," I laughed. "Just try me!"

"You're even prettier when you laugh," he said.

I looked down at my hands, suddenly flustered. It had been a long time since anybody had complimented me, and I'd forgotten how to make a clever answer. It had been an even longer time, I realized with a flush of pleasure, since I had felt pretty.

"I—I guess I better be getting to work," I said, suddenly shy. "I'm late as it is."

274

"Come along, then." He got up, put on his jacket, buckled it. I watched him, frankly enjoying the sight of a big, fine-looking figure of a man in my own kitchen.

As I picked up my coat, I glanced out the window into the sun-drenched street below. The day was clear, bright, full of promise.

Dear God, how good it was to feel like a woman again!